ABOUT THE AUTHOR

Catherine Till grew up in Hungary and came to live in the UK in her early twenties. After a chequered career involving architecture, sinology and handbag design, she became obsessed with shining a light on her native country's recent past through the tale of a family whose lives are buffeted by history as they struggle with their own personal demons.

No Fence
Made
of Sausages

CATHERINE TILL

DIVERGENT PUBLISHING

First published by Divergent Publishing in 2023

Printed and bound in Great Britain by Clays Ltd, Elcograf S.p.A.

ISBN: 978 1 3999 5789 2

For the memory of my brother and my parents

Oh, Magyar, keep immovably
your native country's trust,
for it has borne you, and at death
will consecrate your dust!

No other spot in all the world
can touch your heart as home—
let fortune bless or fortune curse,
from hence you shall not roam!

Mihály Vörösmarty: *Appeal* (1836)
Tr. by Theresa Pulszky; John Edward Taylor

I sat there on the quayside by the landing,
A melon rind was drifting on the flow.
I delved into my fate, now understanding:
the surface chatters and it's calm below.
As if my heart had been its very source,
Troubled, wise was the Danube, mighty force.
       . . .
For hundred thousand years I have been gazing
and suddenly I see what's there to see.
A flash, and time is fully grown, embracing
what generations scan and show to me

Attila József: *By the Danube* (1936)
Tr. by Peter Zollman

1

Escape

Rika was sitting bolt upright next to the window in the train compartment, her lower legs, clad in bell bottoms with sharply ironed creases, were at a precise ninety degrees to the seat and her thighs. Like a seated figure in Egyptian paintings or a minimalist chair without its hind legs, she mused, trying to lighten her own mood.

The express train had just left the outskirts of Budapest and was making its way westwards at a speed that belied its name. This would be a very long two hours. She hoped she would be able to maintain her posture and hold herself together as long as necessary. She had to concentrate, she had to make her story believable. If they started questioning her, they might not accept her excuses. If they searched her, all would be lost.

She tried to put out of her mind that awful, wrenching farewell at the railway station. Gábor was the only one there to see her off, the only person who knew, and the only person she was heartbroken to leave. They both tried to keep up the brave pretence that it was not for ever, yet they could not be certain.

She wondered now if she had endangered his safety: what if he was interrogated and charged with aiding and abetting? She had to keep her plans secret to evade discovery, but also to avoid putting others at risk. But she had to confide in Gábor. There was nobody else as understanding or sympathetic to her way of thinking.

Walking out of the flat earlier this morning, carrying a suitcase, Rika ran into her mother in the hall. They greeted each other with the superficial civility of two strangers who happened to share a flat. Rika did not say goodbye or mention anything about where she was going. Her mother pretended not to have seen the suitcase and that everything was normal.

From the train window Rika noticed the yellowing autumn leaves that had appeared early after this unusually hot summer of 1976 and it dawned on her how long it took to get to this point. She thought about all the hurdles she had to get over for a once-every-three-years chance of a trip to the West. First, putting in a request for hard currency, early in the calendar year before the limited yearly budget ran out, otherwise she would have to wait for another year. Then, getting permission from her workplace to be away. Then, obtaining an exit permit, without which she couldn't actually leave the country, despite having a valid passport to the West. Then, applying for the visa. Rika remembered the interview at the British Embassy when she tried to convince the affable Consul in her far from perfect English that she could make the allocated $50 last for a two-week holiday. It must have worked because she got the visa a month later. And finally, buying the train ticket to London, with the explanation, fortunately accepted, that she would be hitch-hiking on her return.

Numb from sitting like a statue, Rika rocked in her seat to ease the pressure on her bottom. Could she risk standing up and walking to the toilet? She scanned the faces of the people in the compartment. Engrossed in her own problem she hadn't paid any attention to them. Would they tell on her? She couldn't discern sympathy from their demeanours, so to be on the safe side she stayed put. Anyway, it wouldn't be long now, she reckoned; the last station they had passed through was Győr, they would soon be at the border. She got out a sandwich from her canvas satchel, thinking the food would soak up her nervousness. Half way through her munching the train came to a halt.

She couldn't see much around the track where the train had stopped, no buildings, no trees, only a line of look-out towers crossing the near distance. They had reached 'no man's land', the strip of ground between the actual borders of Hungary and Austria.

A sudden recollection popped into her mind: making her way across the same stretch of land from the other direction when she returned from her English holiday three years before. She had got a lift from a Greek lorry driver from the port of Ostend right up to Nickelsdorf on the Austrian side of the border. He didn't want to take her any further for fear of complications. As she spoke neither Greek nor German, she couldn't change his mind. After getting off from the lorry and through the Austrian border check point, she had to walk carrying her backpack along the almost empty road, hemmed in by wire fences. To the left and right she spotted a long traverse line of metal watch-towers diminishing into the horizon and she could make out soldiers with weapons on the high platforms.

She remembered now what she thought at that time, when she was walking towards the Hungarian border post. What kind of a country wants to keep its people from leaving? Even by force?! And then the fear stalking her mind: if I go back, I may not be allowed out again. But her feet carried her forward, automatically, and she realised it was already too late, she had crossed the half way line and could no longer turn around.

Outside the train window now she could make out armed soldiers marshalling Alsatian dogs and she glimpsed a man being escorted off the train. She heard the voices of people coming down the corridor of the train inspecting the compartments. She wrapped up the unfinished sandwich and put it back into the satchel, her fingers struggling with the buckle. Her mouth was dry and she feared everybody around could hear her heart beating in her throat. She tried to take deep breaths without attracting attention to herself and dried her palms on her jeans.

The railway ticket inspector and two burly, armed border guards appeared at the door: 'Passports and tickets, please!' They shone a torch under the seats, looking for stowaways. They checked methodically the passengers and their documents. The smell of sweaty bodies in slept-in uniforms hit Rika's nostrils. She watched as they scrutinised the passport of the woman next to the door, rummaged through the luggage of a young couple two seats away and aggressively body-searched the long-haired man sitting opposite.

Seeing the thoroughness of the inspections as they got closer to her, Rika became convinced there was no chance she could slip through. They would notice that her train ticket was only for a one-way journey, spot the unseasonal clothes in her suitcase, find her university record book and the extra dollars she bought on the black market. They would conclude that she was trying to defect, and she would be charged and put in prison. With all her strength she concentrated on not fainting.

At last her turn came. She handed over her passport and train ticket, and waited for the inevitable.

But now, all of a sudden, the guards appeared impatient to go on to the next compartment. 'Hurry up, Jóska, ...' muttered the larger, more senior looking one to his colleague. 'We still have the third of the train to check. You don't want the boss to ...' His voice trailed off, he clearly realised he shouldn't have spoken in front of civilians. So they just checked if Rika had the exit permit stamped in her passport and held a valid ticket for the current journey, then wished them all a pleasant trip and left the compartment without delay.

Rika was stunned. She could hardly believe what'd happened. What luck! Were the gods that she didn't believe in looking out for her? Or was it just grass-roots incompetence unravelling the web of control? Even so, she felt it was too soon to relax, they were not over the border yet.

After a document inspection by Austrian officials and what seemed like an eternity but in reality perhaps only fifteen minutes' wait, the train started moving again, now at greater speed. When they'd whizzed through several stations so fast that she couldn't read their names properly, only guess they were not Hungarian any more, she judged it safe to get up and gingerly made her way to the toilet.

With the door securely bolted she sat down on the closed lid of the toilet, took her little nail scissors out of her satchel and carefully unpicked the stitches that attached the spine of her university record book to the back crease of her flared jeans. Her ruse had worked. She had managed to smuggle out the object that could help her future in England, the discovery of which would have unmasked her whole plan and landed her in jail.

As she put the record book and the scissors back into her satchel the relief was so overwhelming that she broke down crying, the stress of the past three hours, of the last week, of the previous few months, dissolving into tears. Through waves of sobs she heard the faint loudspeaker announcement that the train would soon be arriving in Vienna. When her emotions subsided a little she blew her nose, mopped her eyes and face, and walked back to the compartment, getting ready to change trains. After an overnight journey in a *couchette* she would wake up the next day in Ostend, then change onto the ferry to Dover, from where another train would take her to London.

2

In the Old Days

Born a few days before Christmas and brought home from the hospital on Christmas Eve, baby Mária was laid under the tree, a small swaddled bundle among shiny colourful packages. A precious present for her parents and sister, four-year-old Blondie.

Mária's father, László, felt he had cheated fate again. When he had been recuperating from his war injury the doctors advised him not to get married and have children, because in all likelihood he would not see them growing up. The fragment of a bullet embedded in his skull was inoperable and could end his life any time. He had frequent blackouts and was warned off drink as it could precipitate an attack. Although he ignored the first part of the doctors' advice, as a responsible young family man he scrupulously stayed off alcohol, even in family celebrations.

László was born at the end of the nineteenth century in Kolozsvár, the main town in Transylvania, which at the time was part of Hungary, the junior partner in the Austro-Hungarian dual monarchy.

He came from impoverished minor gentry; the family surname, Hargitay, once had a noble forename, indicating a proprietorial link with a particular place, but any property had long since been lost. His father was a locksmith on the railways and died in an accident when László was fourteen. He could only attend the local Catholic *gimnázium* with substantial help from charity donations. Then in 1916, his penultimate year at school, László enlisted and went to war.

He never spoke of his war experiences. Whether it was due to memory loss, unconscious suppression or conscious avoidance, nobody knew. The bare facts were that by the time the First World War came to an end he had suffered a head injury with lifelong consequences and his birthplace had become part of another country. Greater Hungary lost two thirds of its territory and had become truncated Hungary. After a long recovery László was given a chance, as a disabled ex-soldier, to complete his education. Following an accelerated accounting course he got an official position in a provincial town, working for the Ministry of Finance as a junior clerk.

László met Lizi in circumstances straight out of a nineteenth century romantic novel. Lizi, under the pretence of dusting the parlour furniture, watched daily from their upstairs window the good looking young man, with a melancholy air, returning to his lodgings in the house opposite. After a few months of surreptitious spying through lace curtains Lizi contrived a chance meeting, involving a dropped handkerchief, on the street in front of their house. A period of proper courtship followed, with chaperoned visits and outings, and in due course marriage, despite her family's misgivings. They settled down in a large county town in south-west Hungary, where their two daughters were born.

In August 1940 Northern Transylvania was given back to Hungary by the Second Vienna Award. The whole country rejoiced, believing this was the beginning of the return of all the territories taken away in the Trianon Treaty at the end of the First World War.

László watched the newsreels in the cinema. He saw Governor Horthy riding into Kolozsvár on his white horse, to the rapturous welcome of the patriotic local population. The people were dressed in traditional costumes, the women wore headdresses and the men cockades in the red-white-green of the Hungarian tricolor. *Erdélyt vissza, mindent vissza,* chanted the flag-waving crowds, demanding the return of the whole of Transylvania and all the other lost lands. Then came the parade of Hungarian troops marching into the town, soldiers with rifles on their shoulders, followed by cavalry and tanks.

He recognised the familiar sights of his youth on the screen. The church and the equestrian statue of King Matthias on the main square, the town hall and the museum in the background. On the dais Governor Horthy welcomed the regained territories. *After twenty-two years of bitter affliction our hopes have become reality ... we have never given up ... standing here on the free land of free Transylvania ... the magnificence of this historic moment ... every Magyar is here in spirit ... with heartfelt love we think of those brothers who have not yet returned to their ancient homeland ...*

Tears streaming down his face, László was seized by an

irrepressible ache to return to his birthplace, to the town he left at seventeen, where his widowed mother and married sister still lived.

But his wife, Lizi, was reluctant to uproot the family. 'We are well settled here. You have a good position and the girls like their school and their friends, so why move?'

'That's where I belong, my love, that's my home ... and now I have a chance to return. I thought you'd understand. I'd like to see my mother, before ... She's getting very frail, my love, you remember what my sister Ilona had written.'

In the end Lizi consented. László requested a transfer at his work place, which fitted in with the aims of the Hungarian government wanting to extend their administrative reach to the newly regained territories. The family moved to Kolozsvár.

They were now comfortably off. László's official title was Financial Counsellor. The local newspapers often carried notices and reports of his presiding over public meetings, intended to promote government initiatives. They lived on the recently renamed Horthy Road, not far from the centre of town. Blondie and Mária attended the Roman Catholic *gimnázium* for girls, took private piano and singing lessons and went in for swimming competitions.

Mária, a lively and sociable girl, soon attracted a small gang of friends, who lived in the neighbourhood. After school she would cycle off to the bank of the Szamos and return in the evening surrounded by a gaggle of adoring older boys. One of them, the winner of the daily contest, was proudly pushing her bicycle.

Lizi was worried about her pre-pubescent daughter's

reputation and 'loss of innocence' in these unchaperoned outings and wanted to put a stop to them. But László wisely observed, 'You don't need to worry, my love, while she is escorted by four or five boys. Save your vigilance for the time when she is walked home by one boy alone.'

One photo from this time showed thirteen-year-old Mária, sitting in a wicker armchair in the garden, cuddling her pet rabbit. She's dressed as a character in a popular operetta, a role she had just performed in an amateur production. Another time she was snapped at the local Lido, wearing a long wrapper after a swim, looking at the photographer with an enchanting smile, while in the background two men can be seen turning back as they pass, unable to take their eyes of her.

Although Mária was prettier and more popular than her sister, but as Blondie was four years older, she was the one the young men came to the house to court. Annoyed at not being the centre of attention Mária tried to remedy the situation. One day when one of her sister's suitors was paying a visit, she burst into the parlour triumphantly brandishing her sister's suspenders. 'Look at me! Look what I have got!' Lizi, who was chaperoning Blondie during the young man's visit, was not amused, and hurriedly bundled her younger daughter and the offending item out of the room, her eyes threatening appropriate punishment.

The return to Kolozsvár, László's lost paradise, lasted barely four years. During the summer of 1944, as the Russian front was approaching from the east, all government offices, among them László's workplace, evacuated to Budapest.

The contents of the family house were packed up into two railway wagons. Lizi and her daughters went ahead, with a suitcase each, to stay with Lizi's mother. The plan was for László to follow them later, accompanying the wagons that held all their furniture and possessions.

The advance of the front, however, turned out to be much faster than anyone had anticipated. In October Kolozsvár was captured by Soviet and Romanian troops. László had to abandon their previous plans, leave all their belongings behind and flee for his life. He turned up in Budapest with only what he could carry.

By November the Soviet forces were pressing on the eastern outskirts of Budapest. László's workplace was evacuated again, this time to Sopron, a small town near the border with Austria. By the following April the 'liberating' Red Army was nearing the westernmost part of Hungary. The family now had no choice left. If they wanted to get out of the way of Soviet troops – with their reputation for rape and looting and for taking men away for *malenkij robot* to the Soviet Union – there was nowhere to go but across the border.

László, Lizi and the girls, were initially held in a *lager* for refugees, then placed temporarily with a farming family in the countryside near Vienna. Lizi and her daughters spoke passable German and were resourceful and practical. Lizi taught the Austrian housewife how to cook tasty stews from onion and potatoes, with some smuggled-out Hungarian paprika. The girls herded the cows to pasture and helped in the kitchen garden, disproving the farmer's prejudices about the preciousness of 'city ladies'.

A few months later they were allowed to travel further west to Vöcklabruck, in the American occupation sector. To earn a living in their new 'home' Lizi and her daughters hit on the idea of making puppets and dolls out of fabric scraps, and twice a week the girls took them to the market in the nearby town. The orders from shops grew quickly and soon they couldn't produce the goods fast enough. To avoid having to walk an hour each way, Blondie and Mária, spirited and enterprising teenagers, often hitched rides in the jeeps of American GIs. But they fearfully declined the lift if it was offered by black soldiers, the likes of which they had never seen before.

While the women coped, even thrived in this temporary, yet seemingly interminable situation, László felt out of place. He had no head for languages, couldn't communicate in German, and felt isolated and useless. He was deeply unhappy. 'I've been forced out of the town of my birth for the second time in my life. And now I have been chased out of my motherland too. How can I survive anywhere else?' he lamented. So when rumours started circulating among the refugees in Austria that there would be an amnesty for the people who returned and they could get their previous jobs back, László set out for Hungary to find out.

The first stop of his reconnaissance was the town of Sopron, where they had briefly lived before escaping to Austria. After he had received reassurances about his job he sent a message to Lizi for them to follow him. 'You should barter the puppets for food and bring as much as you can,' he suggested. In the days of *Milpengő* and *Bilpengő*, when the banknotes had denominations of millions and billions, and monthly salaries had to be spent immediately on receipt to stop it losing value, there was nothing more valuable than food.

The women made their way back to László with food-stuffed suitcases. They lived in Sopron for several months – Mária sent her sixteenth birthday photo to her grandmother from there – before going to Budapest to take refuge with Lizi's family.

*

Katus was born in mercantile Pest in the first year of the twentieth century. Her mother had died when she was little and her father, a bookbinder by trade, remarried a few years later. Being a girl, she was regarded as a convenient nursemaid to her younger brothers and was not formally schooled beyond the age of twelve, the compulsory elementary education level before the First World War. But she was bright and eager for knowledge: she read her brothers' schoolbooks in secret and hung around as they learnt their lessons by rote, her sponge-like mind soaking up all she had overheard. After the boys had left for boarding school she consciously educated herself by devouring any books she could lay her hands on.

Katus had just turned nineteen when in March 1919, after a coup d'etat, the Republic of Soviets was proclaimed in Hungary. The declared aim of this new, Communist-dominated government was the setting up of the dictatorship of the proletariat, but as it also promised to recover all the territories lost in the war, it found universal support in the country. After the enthusiastic, hope-filled first month, however, the prohibition of alcohol led to a widespread breaking of the law and resistance grew everywhere at the confiscation of small businesses their owners had worked hard to acquire. The Communist government reacted with increasing violence, sending its Red Guards to investigate and mete out punishment to suspected counter-revolutionary activities.

Katus's father had by this time built up a small paper-goods business set up in the courtyard of a central Budapest apartment building. They had heard about the requisitioning commandos roaming the capital, but thought they were safe because only enterprises with more than twenty employees were being taken into public ownership.

One morning Katus was in the shop helping her father when three armed, leather-jacketed men burst in. Without saying who they were, the tallest of them, obviously the leader, got straight to the point. 'Are you the owner?' he asked, pointing his rifle at Katus's father.

'Yes, I am. This is my business, ... Comrade,' he said, getting up from his desk. 'My daughter is giving me a hand with the paperwork,' he continued, moving protectively in front of Katus.

'Where are your workers?'

'Our four workmen are in the workshop next door.' Katus stepped out from behind her father, thinking she would be able to deal better with the men herself. 'Shall I call them over?'

'We want to investigate things ourselves,' said the leader, kicking open the door leading into the workshop. He left behind his two comrades, who guarded Katus and her father with raised guns. As she noticed her father's legs starting to buckle, Katus pushed a chair over for him to sit down.

After a few minutes the leader returned. 'Where are you hiding all the other labourers? Have you sent them home?'

'We have no other employees,' said Katus, but the men didn't believe her.

'Show us your accounts, we'll soon find out the truth,' one of the thugs demanded.

One of the others rifle-nudged her father, 'Open the safe, you bourgeois swine, let's see what you have stolen.'

Katus's father fished the key out from a drawer, but his shaking hand couldn't find the keyhole without his daughter's help. They protested that the money in the safe was the workers' wages, due to be paid out to them at the end of the week. It made no difference. The visitors pocketed the money, took away the bundled-up books for examination and left, threatening to return.

Katus and her father realised afterwards that they were lucky to have escaped from this confrontation so lightly, but the episode had created a life-long anti-communist resentment in them, and they were not sorry when this political experiment in the country ended two months later.

When Katus reached the age of twenty-six still unmarried, her father became eager to get his spinster daughter off his hands and introduced her to a friend of the family. After the briefest of courtships Katus consented to marrying József, impatient to start a life and a family of her own.

József and Katus settled down in Kőbánya, one of Budapest's working class suburbs. They soon had two sons,

Tamás and Pál, born a couple of years apart at the end of the 1920s. Though József had a good trade – he was a master carpenter and joiner – his drinking made serious dents in the family's livelihood. Katus eked out their income with sawing beautiful, hand-stitched poplin shirts for other people.

She often had to ask for help from her father, whose small business had grown in the meantime and was providing a respectable income. Many of the non-essential expenses, such as sessions at a professional photographer's studio to chronicle the boys' growing up, were paid for by Katus's father. The photographs of the two little boys, wearing identical short sailor suits and riding a tricycle or a rocking horse, were then presented to their grandfather as gifts.

Despite her reduced circumstances and their lack of money, Katus tried to maintain high standards in their lives. This was her attempt to recreate the values of the middle class background from which she felt she'd been expelled on being married off. Her frugal housekeeping made the most of their modest income – what was left over after József's drinking binges – and she made preserves, patched up clothes and learned to repair anything broken. She kept their small, plainly furnished flat always clean and tidy, despite the contrary tendency of her boys and her husband.

She stressed the importance of reading and education for her sons and supervised their studies. The boys were doing their homework at the kitchen table, while she cooked or sewed. She hoped they would achieve what she as a girl was not allowed to and dreamed that one day they would go to university. To make it possible for them to attend a good school she appealed to her father to cover the boys' tuition fees. She was happy when Tamás, and a couple of years later Pál, passed the entrance exam and got into the local *gimnázium*. Katus's ambition for her sons was on track towards fulfilment.

After Hungary's military involvement in the Second World War started in the summer of 1941, Kőbánya, a semi-industrial district along the railway line, could expect to take heavy hits by enemy forces.

As it happened, there was a huge underground system of caves and tunnels in the area, left behind after the limestone quarries, that gave the area its name, had closed down. These cavernous and temperate spaces were last used by a local brewery for making and storing beer. Then at the beginning of the war the assembly of aircraft engines was moved over from the vulnerable factory on Csepel Island to the undetectable mines of Kőbánya.

Other parts of the tunnel system were fitted out by the civil defence league to provide bomb and gas-proof shelters to civilians during the air raids. Katus wanted her family to take advantage of these hiding places. At first her husband and sons thought the precautions totally unnecessary and her needlessly alarmist. But as the aerial attacks became more frequent, her nagging to get them to the shelter on hearing the warning sirens gradually found receptive ears.

She had prepared small emergency packs for each of them – with cigarettes in József's, books and candles in her sons' and food and water in hers – just waiting inside their front door to be grabbed when they had to run to the tunnels. In the winter she added rolls of blankets. When they had to stay in the shelter overnight or longer, Katus slipped outside between the raids with her eldest son, Tamás, and brought back provisions.

They survived, thanks to these precautions, physically unharmed but in a permanent state of hunger and fear for their lives. The boys attended school when it was not closed for shortage of teachers or lack of coal for heating or bomb damage. József did whatever work he could find – not much call for fine carpentry skills in wartime – either badly paid or bartered for food. Katus managed to hold their lives together on even less than a shoestring.

In April 1944, two weeks after the Germans occupied Hungary, the Allied bombing started in earnest, targeting major railway stations, factories and oil refineries, and carpet bombing extended areas.

Seventeen-year-old Tamás, along with his peers, was summoned to the Military Academy for a medical examination, preliminary to being called up and sent to the Russian front. As he and his classmates saw it, this was clearly a desperate attempt by the occupying Germans and their reluctantly compliant Hungarian allies to turn the fortunes of the war. Almost certainly futile, almost certainly fatal for the conscripts, and to be avoided at all costs. But how to get out of it?

Tamás was advised by a friendly doctor to down several strong coffees before the medical examination. 'You'll have an irregular heartbeat and they will pronounce you unfit to be conscripted.'

He shared this information with his friends, but many of

them, either ignoring the advice or not as lucky with the military doctors as him, were drafted into the army and taken to the front. Some not returned for years, some never came back at all.

By early November 1944 the Soviet troops were approaching the eastern edge of Budapest. The occupying German forces dug their heels in and thought they could halt the advance of the Red Army. In the fierce bombardments that followed the house next to where Katus and József lived took a direct hit.

József, who had seven siblings, suggested that they seek refuge with his relatives in the city where he was born. 'Esztergom is not so vulnerable, it's not in the front line, and we will not be in the crossfire between the Germans and the Russians. Somebody will be able to put us up, one of my brothers or sisters.'

Katus did not need much persuading. The problem was how to make the less than 50 kilometre journey. Most trains were diverted to the war effort and the railway lines were liable to be bombed. Katus sought help from her father again and they finally escaped from the capital in a small lorry from her father's business.

Although Esztergom was not as unaffected by the fighting as József had previously thought, they safely made it to the end of the war and did not return to the capital until early April, after the victory of the Soviet troops.

Back in Budapest with his family Tamás finished his last year at the *gimnázium* and passed the *érettségi* with top marks. The road to further studies lay open to him.

As it happened, the newly-minted Hungarian Republic, under Soviet domination, gave young people with the correct class credentials the chance to study at university. Tamás could demonstrate that he fell into the right category: he was born in the working class district of Kőbánya and his father, a carpenter, was a manual worker. He kept quiet about the fact that his maternal grandfather owned a small paper goods factory.

He enrolled on an electrical engineering course at Budapest Technical University. He was clever and did well in his studies, the high standards instilled in him by his mother bearing results. Success came easy to him and this gave him boundless self-confidence. When asked in an exam to recall an important technical measurement, he replied cockily: 'I don't remember it, but I can cite the title of several reference books where one can easily look it up.' Surprisingly, he did not fail the exam.

*

When the families of Tamás and of Mária returned to Budapest they found the capital hardly recognisable.

The city that emerged from the last-ditch battle between the German and Soviet forces and the fifty-day-long siege by the Red Army was devastated. No building was left undamaged, not only along railway lines and in industrial areas but also in residential districts and suburbs. The stars of pre-war picture postcards of the Pearl of the Danube – Buda Castle and the Matthias Church, the Parliament and the Basilica, the Opera House and the Millennium Monument – lay in ruins. All seven bridges across the river were wrecked beyond use, having been blown up by the retreating German troops. Their bridgeheads were leaning into the water along the shores of the Danube like so many ghosts patiently awaiting resurrection.

Post-war reconstruction couldn't begin while the two sides of the city were cut off from each other. As soon as the fighting had stopped temporary pontoon bridges were constructed to connect Buda and Pest, but these were destroyed by the huge slabs of ice drifting down the river during the following hard winter. After a heroically accelerated effort the first of the completely rebuilt, permanent bridges – the former Franz Joseph, now renamed Liberty – was finally opened to traffic in August 1946, presided over with triumphant ceremony by the occupying Soviet troops.

3

Into a New Era

Through the gappy fence Tamás caught glimpses of a petite, Madonna-faced girl with sexy eyebrows. In a pinafore-dress, her hair in a short wavy bob, she was hanging out freshly-washed clothes in the dusty yard and singing a popular, cooing, wartime love-song. *Every minute I think of you a hundred times.*

He did not know if he should curse his bad luck or thank his lucky stars. He was in the last few days of his university vacation, staying at Lake Balaton with his girlfriend, when out of the blue this little beauty had turned up, the granddaughter of the elderly lady next door. Unable to get her out of his head, he engineered a chance meeting with the girl – called Mária, fittingly, he thought. To his frustration their acquaintance could go no further than hurried conversations at the lake-side behind his jealous girlfriend's back, but at least he managed to get the girl's address. Returning to Budapest after the holiday he broke up with his girlfriend and started visiting Mária.

For Tamás going from his home in the Kőbánya district to see

Mária on the other side of the Danube was not an easy undertaking. The only reliable link between the two sides of the city was Liberty Bridge, rebuilt and reopened a year ago. To seek out the girl with the lovely smile, who so captivated him, meant a long, complicated journey, with many changes, northwards on the Pest side, bogged down in queuing, snail-like traffic on the bridge and then southbound in Buda, mentally urging the bus to go faster to get to her sooner.

Turning up to introduce himself to her parents Tamás discovered that Mária, a schoolgirl of not yet seventeen, was already the centre of attention of a trio of eligible young men. She would go around with one tall beau on either arm and one lagging behind, escorting her to the cinema, taking her dancing or accompanying her to swimming in the Danube. Tamás, though slim and not bad-looking, was no match in stature for these sporty admirers, but he was not deterred and threw himself into the contest with relish.

Mária's mother, Lizi, unashamedly subjected the newcomer to a questioning worthy of an experienced detective. Tamás did not have a lot of things in his favour. He was from a working class district on the less salubrious side of the Danube. Having a carpenter for a father may have been an advantageous background in the current regime, as his university place had already proved, but not in Lizi's eyes. She would have preferred a son of a lawyer or a doctor as a potential son-in-law. And while he might have good prospects as an engineer, that was still some years in the future.

It was thanks to the quiet, behind-the-scenes influence of László, Mária's father, over his usually dominant wife that

Tamás was not sent packing after the first visit. 'I wasn't much of a catch, my love, when we met,' he said to Lizi. 'Allow the young man a chance to prove himself.'

Lizi remembered her own young man from twenty-odd years before, who emerged from the First World War with a serious head injury and with his home-town lost to another country. László was starting to rebuild his life in rump Hungary, when Lizi fell in love with the shy young clerk. Her family had objected to him at first and she had to fight them, fight for him. But they were wrong and her instinctive feelings about him had been proved right. Softened by her memories and heeding the wise words of her reticent husband, she relented and eased up on her vetting of Tamás.

Mária and her family had arrived in Budapest a few months before, after an almost three-year-long odyssey. They lived in Kolozsvár during the war and had to leave their home as the front approached from the east. Fleeing before the advance of the Red Army, they moved further and further westwards, eventually crossing into Austria.

By now all that was mixed memories for Mária. She tried not to think of the frightening escape across the freezing border, hungry and afraid of being shot at, and their dismal first days in the *lager*, when they did not know what their fate would be. What she had remembered was what came after – all adventures for her fourteen-year-old self. The novelty of living in the countryside on that Viennese farm and the fun she and her sister Blondie had helping out. And when they moved to western Austria, the weekly trips to the market to sell the harlequin puppets and catching lifts from flirtatious American soldiers to save walking five kilometres there and back.

They could have stayed and made a life for themselves there, if it had not been for her father, who simply could not imagine living outside of his mother country.

As Lizi and her daughters made their way back to Hungary, Blondie met a handsome young man among the returning refugees. Alfréd looked her up after they'd settled in Budapest and courted her with such romantic intensity that Blondie was swept off her feet in a matter of weeks.

Her family was less charmed by him. Alfréd was highly strung and appeared to be prone to fainting fits, which Mária secretly suspected were shams. She observed him during one of his attacks, and caught him half-opening an eye to check the effect of his dramatic performance on the spectators. She did not trust him after this discovery.

Blondie, however, wouldn't hear a word said against Alfréd and they secretly got married. As she was over the legal age for marriage her parents had no choice but to accept the *fait accompli*, but Mária would leave the room whenever her new brother-in-law entered.

Blondie's brief happiness came to an end with an unexpected visit from a woman who claimed and was proved to be Alfréd's first wife. He maintained that as he had married the woman while they were refugees in Austria the marriage was not legal in Hungary, so strictly speaking he was not a bigamist. The law, however, said otherwise, Alfréd went to prison and Blondie's marriage was annulled.

Blondie's emotional recovery from this disastrous liaison took the shape of a brief shoe buying obsession and a rebound correspondence with a prisoner of war who was still being held in a labour camp in the Soviet Union. Tibor finally came back to Budapest three years after the end of war, emaciated and with several teeth missing. He was older, taciturn and gruff, entirely different from the charming Alfréd, but it all worked in his favour with Blondie.

After their return from Austria, Mária was able to restart her interrupted and much delayed education. She was not academically inclined and wanted to study practical subjects. Her mother enrolled her at a religious, vocational school for girls, where in addition to the usual *gimnázium* curriculum the nuns taught foreign languages, typing and shorthand, sewing and household management. In 1948, after Mária's first year there, all religious schools were nationalised, but the nuns were able to continue till graduation with their current pupils.

Having settled into a life in peace and school in Budapest, Mária enjoyed being courted by the young men around her, brothers of her classmates or sons of family friends. She felt it was compensation for the experiences of the past few years and no less than her due. When Tamás arrived on the scene, having finished with his girlfriend, Mária was flattered by his single-minded attention. He visited her whenever he could, at weekends or slipping away from his classes at university, which was conveniently situated just next to Liberty Bridge, halfway on his route between his home and hers.

Tamás was different from Mária's other admirers. He was

less conventional, more intellectual, and he impressed her from the start. She liked that he was not as tall as her other suitors, so she didn't have to crane her neck as much when looking at him. She did not mind that he was not sporty or much of a dancer, she became attracted by his lively, questioning mind. Looking into his mesmerising blue eyes she felt special that he had chosen her.

Seeing his persistence and her growing and unmistakeable preference for him, his rivals had gradually dropped away, one after the other leaving the contest and the prize to him..

Two years after their first meeting Mária gave him a photo of herself – sunbathing in a decorous two-piece swimsuit but in a starlet pose – inscribing it on the back with 'To Tamás with true love'. He had won her over. But she was still at school and he had not finished university, so they had to wait.

Tamás and Mária were finally married in 1951, a month before her twenty-first birthday, and after he had graduated and got a job on the factory-island of Csepel.

On their wedding photo Mária did look like her namesake, in a long demure white dress and veil, with a shy, happy smile on her lips and a bunch of lilies in her arms. Tamás, his hairline already receding to a high forehead, in a dark suit, with a protective arm around his bride and a cat-that-got-the-cream expression on his face.

Their life together started in Buda. They found a sublet in a turn-of-the-century building, still pockmarked by bullet holes from the siege of Budapest at the end of the war. The street was dark, the sun only brushed the five-storey-tall façades briefly around noon. Their widowed landlady rented out one of the street-facing rooms in her flat for them to live in and the small room next to the kitchen – the maid's in former times – for Tamás's workshop. Sharing the bathroom and the kitchen with Aunty Ella, who wasn't a relative, merely addressed so out of respect, demanded continual diplomacy on Mária's part, although their relationship was friendly.

All their family life was condensed into one room: the convertible sofa served as the marital bedroom, the armchairs and the table in front of it their living and dining room, with a baby cot and later a child's divan bed in the corner as the nursery. There was a big-valve radio set built by Tamás on a table next to the sofa, a huge wardrobe on the opposite wall and often clothes were drying in front of the iron stove. At Christmas time they even managed to squeeze a two-metre-high tree into their one room living space.

Their first child was born eight and a half months after the wedding. Tamás was at work on that Saturday morning when the factory loudspeaker came through to the engineers' cubicle. 'Comrade Varga, please come to the office.' There was a phone call waiting for him from the hospital. They informed him that during the night his wife gave birth to a little girl.

Baby Marika, named after her mother, was under-weight, tiny and delicate. Mária had to express her milk and use a medicine dropper to feed her newborn, who was too weak to suckle. She always referred to her daughter as a 'premature baby'.

In the mornings Tamás left for work early. After a short lie-in Mária would feed her daughter and get her ready, and then go down with the pram in the clanking, metal-caged lift to do her shopping. Their residential street branched off from a winding, shop-lined boulevard, with a tram-track running in the middle. She was glad to get out of the dark flat, to take the baby for some air and sunshine and to have a chat with other mothers in the handkerchief-sized park on the opposite side of the boulevard. It was a brief respite before going back to the cooking, the hand-washing of nappies and the daily fire-building in the iron stove.

Tamás worked as an electrical engineer in a state-run factory – there were no other kinds – and in his spare time ran a small, needless to say, illegal business from home. He repaired electrical equipment, such as Grundig tape recorders or state-of-the-art transistor radios, brought back to Hungary by successful sportsmen, the only people permitted to travel to the West in the 1950s.

On evenings when a client of Tamás's was expected to drop in bringing something that needed repair, Aunty Ella, alerted by Mária, would hover in the hall, dressed in her best frock, engaged in some urgent and essential piece of housework. She couldn't be beaten in answering the doorbell first and showing the handsome young celebrities into Tamás's workshop. 'Where else can you meet an Olympic gold medallist fencer or a World Champion water-polo player?' she explained to Mária.

The private jobs Tamás took on were necessary to make ends meet. His salary had to support the whole growing family, as contrary to the Communist ethos he did not want his wife to go out to work. He believed in the traditional roles of the man as the main breadwinner and the woman as mother and home-maker. They quarrelled about Mária not budgeting well enough when the housekeeping money didn't stretch till the end of the month, but when Tamás set out to demonstrate how it should be done, the money ran out after a week.

'In the old days before the war there were rich and poor; now everybody is poor,' remarked Tamás's mother, Katus, acerbically. Her dislike of the Communists was born of her experiences during the short-lived Republic of Soviets after the First World War. The current government seemed to be their successors – one of the Commissars from 1919 was now the Party Secretary – and they were continuing the same policies. They have finally nationalised her father's small paper factory, this time without having to send leather-jacketed thugs to take money out of the till, but confiscating everything.

To finance after-war rebuilding and industrial investment in the country, every year workers were expected to buy, at the cost of a month's salary, state issued *Békekölcsön*. 'They call them peace bonds, yet you can't sell them or cash them in, they are just another pretext to take money out of people's pocket,' complained Tamás, but only in private to his wife.

After he came home from the factory and eaten what Mária re-heated for him from the family's midday meal, Tamás settled down in one of the armchairs to read the paper. Amid the often repeated non-news, of factory openings or overproduction of quotas, there were items that always got his intellectual hackles up – reports about the construction of locomotives or ships that went straight to the Soviet Union as reparations. He pointed out the contradiction to Mária, when she came back from the kitchen. 'If they are truly our liberators as they present themselves, how come we have to pay compensation to them for war damage, like a defeated nation to the victorious conquerors?'

Another thing most people blamed the government for was economic mismanagement. Years after the war ended there were still shortages and rationing in basic foodstuffs – inconceivable in a country that had always prided itself on producing all the food it needed. The meals Mária cooked consisted mostly of starchy foods and vegetables in flour-fattened sauces. Meat played only an occasional side role; small amounts of it were padded out with breadcrumbs and fried into a *fasírt* to accompany a vegetable *főzelék,* and it was rarely elevated to a star appearance at Sunday lunch. Having grown well-rounded under his wife's cooking and their unavoidable diet, Tamás sometimes caught sight of his slim self in their wedding photo and thought he would no longer fit into that smart suit.

Tamás was getting ahead in his profession fairly quickly. Apart from his own abilities, he put this down to a lucky coincidence. 'Now the country needs freshly trained, capable engineers. And I'm not regarded as a class enemy, with my background, growing up in Kőbánya' he reflected to Mária. Before long he was awarded the title 'Stakhanovite electronic engineer' at work, for his inventions that helped to increase Socialist production. But in the company of friends and family members he always took pains to stress that he hadn't joined the Party, that he opposed the system, while he worked it for the benefit of his family.

As he advanced in his field he was sent by the government – as a reward and a sign of political trust – on several study and cooperation tours to Leipzig and Dresden in the friendly socialist German Democratic Republic. From there he sent loving postcards to his wife and little daughter, to 'Lady Tamás

Varga and Miss Marika', using the pre-Communist formal addresses of *Úrhölgy* and *Kisasszony*, as if they were still currently in use and not politically frowned upon. Mária was worried. Was it wise, using these pre-war titles instead of 'Comrade', on postcards that everyone could see? What if somebody noticed and informed on him? Did he think he was untouchable because the regime needed people like him? If he wasn't careful his cockiness could endanger his family.

Before Marika's second birthday Mária got pregnant again. It was not happy timing: she had had abdominal surgery in the previous months and they were afraid the wound would open up during the pregnancy. But under the population increasing policies of Health Minister Anna Ratkó there was no way out. Mária's medical reasons were not serious enough for the official committee that had to approve all abortions. Their second child, Gábor, was born in due course.

Little Gabi inherited his sister's cot bed and a small divan bed was installed for her in the adjacent corner. Once able to stand by pulling himself up by the railings, Gabi took every opportunity of reaching out from his balustraded domain and grabbing the hair of his passing sister, who regarded it as a hostile attack on her until then unchallenged position. Gabi's first attempts at speaking created a version of his sister's name, Lika, followed by Rika, which became everybody's nickname for her.

Both children were christened. Although the Communist regime's declared aim was the eventual elimination of the power and influence of the church, it was still possible for people to practice their religion, if it was done unobtrusively. But certain precautions had to be observed. Once they received an aid parcel from an aunt of Tamás, who had emigrated to Belgium between the two world wars, and discovered inside, hidden in a tin of milk powder, a silver cross on a chain and a small statue of the Virgin Mary. They were not surprised by the use of this camouflage; it was common knowledge that all foreign parcels were opened and inspected, at least superficially. You couldn't take any chances.

They were not particularly religious or even regular churchgoers. Had Tamás reflected on it he would have described himself as agnostic. But Mária insisted on having the children christened, because she thought 'it was proper' to do so, because 'how would it look if we didn't', and Tamás went along with his wife's wishes. He explained it to his mother, 'Let her have what she wants, it's not worth risking a quarrel.' But secretly he also reckoned that this was the philosophically safest course of action to take. He was familiar with the argument of Pascal's wager: there is nothing to lose if one behaved as if God existed.

In the pervasive atmosphere of repression, with the drab drudgery of everyday living in cramped accommodation amid food shortages, family life and the two-week annual holiday provided the escapist antidotes.

Mária was happily immersed in the day-to-day care of her children. No matter how tired by her chores, she would often entertain them at meals or before bed with silly made-up stories.

One late winter afternoon they were lingering over a supper of small baked potatoes, spread with tasty pork-dripping from the month ago Sunday roast. They were waiting for Tamás to come home from the factory before the children's bedtime. Suddenly darkness fell on the room, one of those not infrequent power-cuts. Mária promptly found the emergency candle and matches, and restored the table to a faint visibility, but one-year-old Gabi became frightened and started crying.

To pacify her son Mária started telling them the story of the crooked-mouthed family, where nobody could blow straight to extinguish a candle. She played all the funny, gurning characters with gusto, inventing as she went along, and the candle on their own table became a prop in the tale.

'First the crooked-mouthed daddy tried, "I'll show you how to do it!"' Here Mária demonstrated the father's action by covering her upper lip with the lower and blowing upwards. She looked like a frog to Rika, who burst out laughing.

'Then the crooked-mouthed mummy tried. "You can't do anything right," she said to the daddy, "this is how to do it."' Mária now did the opposite with her lips and blew downwards. She's a rabbit, thought Rika, now helpless with laughter. Sitting on his mother's lap, little Gabi chuckled, his earlier fear forgotten.

Tamás arrived home to find his wife grimacing and his children giggling around the table in the candlelight. Mária quickly finished the story and put Gabi, falling asleep in her arms, in his cot. Rika wanted to delay bedtime and pestered her parents. 'Apu, have you heard about the crooked-mouth family? Anyu, what happened next?' But she had to go to bed without getting any answers.

Holidays were the only occasions when Tamás could really relax – without the need for constant political alertness – and spend enough time with his small family. For the first few summers they stayed by Lake Balaton with Mária's grandmother, who usually rented a room for a month in a village house. The conditions were basic, there was no bathroom and the whole family slept in one room, but the memory of their first meeting here added to the simple pleasures of the vacation: long lie-ins, sunbathing in the yard, swimming or splashing with the children in the lake and evening walks in the honey-smell of acacia bushes to the fried-fish kiosk near the station.

On a July morning the year after his son was born, Tamás, in swimming trunks with soap in hand and a towel slung over his shoulder, had just returned from bathing in the lake, at the bottom of the lane. It was almost noon. His son's cot bed was already set up in the yard for the day, partly covered by white terry towels to shade it from the strong sun.

With an indulgent smile, Tamás watched his daughter, a nut-brown little imp with sun-bleached hair, chasing the dog and being chased by the geese, that frightened the four-year-old city child. To deflect her from teasing her baby brother, he urged Rika to collect eggs from the hen-house with her great-grandmother and to 'help' with making lunch in the outdoor kitchen.

The rough wooden table in the yard was laid for four. He lifted his son out of his cot and sat down with him on the bench, dandling his son on his knee while waiting for the women to bring the food. Gabi wriggled round in the embrace and struggled to stand up, his windmill arms finding and grabbing hold of his father's ears.

From a radio somewhere nearby floated the sound of the midday bells. As if answering this call for lunch the unmistakable smell of fried onion, peppers and tomatoes wafted from the summer kitchen. Ah, *lecsó*, Tamás sniffed, hoping the women hadn't forgotten to get some extra-hot paprika for him.

Looking up he saw Mária in a faded sun-dress, skin golden-brown, stepping out of the house, squinting, carrying a tray of fizzy drinks and slices of bread in a basket. He watched her walking towards them at the table. His mind was flooded by feelings – holiday contentment, pride in his son and his family, the loveliness of his wife – all crystallising in a single thought. How could he persuade her to have another child?

4

Budapest 1956

Mária was woken up by Gabi's hunger cries, the daily, unvarying baby alarm clock of their lives. She peered towards the window. Grey light was seeping into the back of the room, around the dark silhouette of the wardrobe. It was past daybreak. Tamás was still snoring gently on the bed beside her, short of gunfire from the street nothing would wake him. Suddenly it struck her: she could hear footsteps in the flat, but no sound of fighting coming from outside. Blissful silence, after a week of intermittent battering noise, of wakeful nights and frightened days. She wanted to go back to sleep, to dissolve her exhaustion, but she saw in the dim light that Rika, in her little bed at the foot of theirs, was also awake and would soon want breakfast. She had to get up to feed the children. Luckily, the bathroom happened to be free, so she dressed hurriedly, gathered up Gabi, gave the children a quick cat-lick, and they filed into the kitchen.

Aunty Ella, their landlady, was already there. She had been up since dawn, made coffee and was eager to report all the official and unofficial news she had gathered.

'Did you hear? A ceasefire was announced last night! It seems some of the Soviet tanks have switched side to the rebels and the rest have disappeared from the streets.' She could not hide her excitement. 'They've said on the radio that the government would leave the Warsaw Pact. The revolution is over!'

The silence from the street appeared to offer a confirmation.

Mária gulped down her strong coffee and felt the caffeine lifting the cloud of tiredness in her head. The news was very well but right now she had to feed a grumpy child and a screaming baby. She briskly cooked semolina porridge, in water since they had no milk left, trying to make it palatable by sprinkling a little sugar and cinnamon on it. Rika still ate it reluctantly while it slowly congealed in her bowl. Gabi was not fooled by the usual ruse of the little aeroplane delivering food to his mouth and batted the spoon away, splashing Aunty Ella, who did not take cover in time. Having run out of basics, the apparent stop in the fighting now brought a chance to replenish their food reserves.

As if on cue Tamás, with seven-day stubble and pyjama jacket gaping over his stomach, appeared in the doorway. 'Sweetheart, don't you think it's time you attempted food shopping again?'

Mária was fuming as she made her way down the stairs, the week-long pent up resentment rising to the surface. *Why is it always me having to brave these dangerous, frightening situations? Why couldn't my precious husband do it for a change? Is it beneath his dignity to go shopping? Does he think I'm more dispensable than him? Or is he simply a coward?*

Her silent grumble was interrupted when on the ground floor she ran into the caretaker's wife. 'Mrs Varga, you should hurry, the grocery store at Széna Square is now open. If you're quick you could get bread, milk and eggs before they sell out.'

Opening the heavy street door of the house, Mária popped her head out and looked around cautiously before stepping out. Among the debris covering the middle of their street she saw several round flat objects placed at regular intervals. Ah, this is what Aunty Ella mentioned yesterday, she thought, upturned plates that looked like land-mines from a distance to deter tank drivers going through.

Once out of the house, she turned right, away from the main boulevard, and right again at the corner, hurrying anxiously down a side street. In front of her and on the rubble strewn pavement opposite she noticed a handful of people like her, men and women, scurrying in the same direction with string bags in hand.

Over the previous week the revolution had burst upon their neighbourhood. The winding Margit Boulevard at the end of their street was the connection between Margit Bridge, a strategic point on the bank of the Danube, and Széna Square, one of the centres of resistance. Three days after the initial, peaceful student demonstrations in the middle of Budapest were greeted with police fire, numerous armed opposition groups had sprung up in their district. These freedom fighters occupied several nearby government buildings, one of them a prison. It was rumoured that railway carriages were dragged by the rebels from the Southern Railway Station to Széna Square to serve as reinforcements behind the barricades against the Soviet tanks. The sound of gunfire and explosions of Molotov cocktails kept most people confined to their flats, from where they only emerged for hurried excursions to the shops during the brief lulls in the fighting.

On the 23rd of October, the day it all started, Tamás had gone to work at half past six, as usual. He found his factory deserted, because most of the workers there had joined the demonstrations, so he had returned home. Even though he privately agreed with the demands of the protesters – the withdrawal of Soviet troops from Hungary and the removal of the Communists from the government – he had taken part in none of the events. Like a lot of people, he wouldn't engage in public discussions, saying *nem politizálok*, having learnt that even just talking about politics, casually, outside the circle of family and friends, could land you in trouble. You never knew who might be listening and reporting what you said.

In the days that followed buses and trams disappeared from the streets, so observing the official curfews he stayed at home, waiting to see how things would turn out. There were no daily papers published, Hungarian radio was intermittently off the air and the government's announcements were concealing rather than revealing the true nature of the developments. To learn what was really going on he resorted to listening, illegally, to Radio Free Europe or the BBC.

At the first sounds of fighting in their neighbourhood Tamás had realised that their first-floor, street-facing room was vulnerable to stray bullets or explosions. As a precaution he removed the inside pair of their casement windows, so that if the glass in the outside windows broke, they would still have another pair to replace it with and protect themselves from the cold weather.

He had also moved their beds to the innermost part of the room and they slept there, behind the barricade of the wardrobe pushed in front of the window. During the day the family and their landlady decamped into the kitchen and Tamás's workroom next to it, which both faced the tall internal courtyard of the building and were safe from gunfire. The women cooked what they could from the staples in the pantry and the children played under their feet.

Reaching Széna Square on the morning after the streets had fallen silent Mária saw nothing military. Civilians in autumn coats and hats huddled together, exchanging news, or milling around in the middle of the square inspecting the railway wagons that lay on their sides, partly dismantled or burnt out. Many of the buildings facing the square were badly damaged, the protective rendering on their façades blasted away by explosions or bullets, revealing the bare bricks. There were gaping holes in the street-facing walls at several levels, and in the window openings the glass, sometimes even the frames, were missing. She found it hard to believe people might still be living there.

At the corner of the square in front of the Közért grocery store she saw delivery trucks waiting and men in work-jackets unloading large sacks and boxes. There were no queues forming in front of the shops yet. She rushed across and finished her shopping quickly, buying as much as she could find and thought she could carry, and then set off for home.

The sun came out, only a weak, end-of-October sun, without much warmth, but it still made Mária feel that some change for the better had taken place.

What she saw walking across the square reinforced this feeling. The red-white-green national flag mounted above a doorway had a round hole cut out in the middle – the hammer and sickle were gone. Nailed to one of the still upright railway wagons was a bed sheet painted with the back view of a balding, roly-poly figure, the caricature of the former Communist party leader, heading for the border carrying suitcases labelled 'Stalinist dogmas' and 'Violations of the law'. A small poster underneath gave notice about the first meeting of the Independent Smallholders Party, just legalized again during the past few days. Another handwritten notice invited people, on the eve of All Saint's Day, to light candles in their windows in memory of the fallen revolutionary fighters.

On the far side of the square she spotted a long queue in front of what was clearly not a shop selling food. From this distance she could not see what the attraction was, only that as the queue shortened from the front, it grew from the back. Thinking she had chanced on finding some rarely available, shortage items, she asked a middle-aged couple at the end of the line. 'What's this queue for? What can you buy here?'

'Oh, nothing's for sale here. It's donations to help the families of those who died fighting the Russians. We want to contribute.'

Getting closer Mária discovered at the foot of a wall a large ammunition box, emptied of its original content and now full of paper money. Stuck to the wall above the box were a 100 forint banknote and a handwritten notice. THE PURITY OF OUR REVOLUTION MAKES IT POSSIBLE TO COLLECT MONEY IN THIS WAY FOR THE FAMILIES OF OUR MARTYRS. She saw that the banknote was easy to remove and that nobody kept an eye on the collection.

She was astonished that people had donated so much, when everybody had so little. There must have been hundreds of thousands there in the box, she calculated. It seemed quite unbelievable. When a kilo of bread cost three forints and the four of them lived on Tamás's salary of less than 1300 a month. And the even more surprising thing was that people were not tempted to steal any of it, despite no obvious guarding.

Looking in her purse, she found only a few *fillér* left after her grocery shopping. She felt ashamed that she couldn't give anything, so turned around and hurried back home, as much as her two bags full of shopping allowed her.

Back in the flat Mária was welcomed by the smell of Aunty Ella's *babgulyás*, almost ready now. Her mouth watered at the thought of the bean stew and she realised how hungry she'd become.

Tamás, now dressed but still unshaven, was sitting in his workroom, with a child perched on each knee. In his wife's absence he had to keep an eye on the children, but he didn't want to miss the latest news. So he divided his attention between listening to the radio, looking at a picture book with Rika and trying to prevent Gabi grabbing screwdrivers or soldering irons from his desk.

While unpacking her shopping, including the just acquired

treasure of a dozen eggs, Mária told Aunty Ella and Tamás what she had seen during her shopping foray. Then she set about making some fresh ribbon pasta they would have with poppy seeds and sugar, as the second part of their lunch. *Mákos tészta*, everybody's favourite dish, was always a treat and now there was something celebratory in the air.

After putting the children down for their afternoon nap, Tamás, Mária and Aunty Ella gathered in Tamás's workroom and tuned in to Free Kossuth Radio in time to catch the Prime Minister's message. Imre Nagy, speaking on behalf of the just formed National Government, spoke to the 'workers, peasants and intellectuals' of the country and called the events of the past week a 'revolution'.

'This is most significant!' Tamás cut in with his comment. 'He acknowledges what's happened. Not condemning it, as the previous criminal lot did.'

Imre Nagy pledged the abolition of the one-party system and the complete withdrawal of Soviet troops. He urged the people to go back to work, to collect their salaries for the past month, and promised that the shops would be open, fully stocked and there would be no queues. 'Long live a free, democratic and independent Hungary!' he ended his broadcast.

The next day, the last of October, Tamás went off to work. Reassured and encouraged by the Prime Minister's broadcast, he wanted to collect his salary, without which the family could not survive much longer.

He set out in the morning mist along his customary daily route hoping to catch a bus or a tram that may be back in service.

Reaching his usual tram-stop by the Danube he saw the twisted tracks uprooted from their bedding of paving stones and some mangled carriages further on. Public transport had clearly not been restored yet. He decided to continue on foot.

His journey to work also became one of discovery. On the gable ends of damaged buildings the graffiti RUSSKIES GO HOME had replaced the red star. He saw burned-out armed-vehicles everywhere, piles of rubble strewn all over the streets and lots of corpses, most of them of Soviet soldiers. At the Buda end of Chain Bridge he came upon an undamaged tank, its Hungarian driver leaning out of the turret, chatting with civilians who gathered around offering him bread and cigarettes.

On Liberation Square in Pest he passed the temporary grave of a fallen resistance fighter, the words YOU WILL BE REVENGED painted on the wooden cross. How ironic, he thought, the Russians had us rename this square to commemorate their 'liberation' of Hungary and now, after the past week, it may mark our freedom from them.

Almost two hours after he had set out from home he arrived at his place of work. The offices were open, but the shop-floor was silent and deserted, as workers from the factories of Csepel island had been the main force in the uprising and they had not returned yet. He collected his salary from the Cash Office and was told by Personnel to be back at work for the general re-start on Monday.

During the following few days the situation changed. Tamás, glued to the radio, was listening day and night to both foreign news and the government's messages, trying to piece together what was happening and filling the gaps with hearsay.

The Soviet forces staged ostensible withdrawals, with lines of tanks conspicuously snaking out of major cities.

Then, almost immediately, they returned.

Stories circulated that once outside the border the departing soldiers, demoralized by having to fight a brotherly socialist country, were replaced with freshly indoctrinated, but misinformed troops. It was rumoured that arriving on Hungarian soil the new conscripts asked '*Gdye Suez?*', 'Where is Suez?' and were ready to fight the imperialist aggressors and take back control of the canal.

In a radio address Imre Nagy demanded the departure of the newly arrived troops and asked the United Nations to guarantee Hungary's neutrality. Western broadcasts reported long lines of Soviet tanks pouring back into the country and widespread resistance by the Hungarians.

At dawn on the 4th of November Tamás caught the Prime Minister's impassioned speech on the radio. *Soviet troops are attacking the capital, intent on deposing the Government. The Hungarian forces are resisting. This is what I want the country and the world to know.*

His address was repeated several times in all major world languages before falling abruptly silent at 8 a.m.

In the end, the call for help by the Hungarian government to the United Nations was not heeded and no help arrived. Armed resistance continued, diminishing gradually and lasting the longest in Budapest and in industrial areas. But after barely three weeks the fight for national independence was effectively crushed and Soviet dictatorship, in the words of Radio Free Europe, was established again by overwhelming force.

Ten days into November, the fighting in Budapest had largely died down. In the last couple of days official notices had appeared, posted on the walls of buildings everywhere, in parallel versions of Russian and Hungarian. *Prikaz No.1* of the Commander of Soviet military units in Budapest – invited by the new, Moscow backed government to crush the 'counter-revolution' – ordered the residents of the city to go back to work.

At the same time, as if in a reply, home-made leaflets signed by the 'Youth of Budapest still fighting for independence' were stuck up on street corners and distributed from hand to hand in the neighbourhood. They urged all employees to strike and not to work for the 'occupiers and the illegal, traitor government'.

Monday, the start of a new working week, was looming. Tamás tried to decide what to do. Go back to work or stay away? Much as he was a dissident in his thoughts, much as he sympathised with the 'Youth of Budapest', what would a strike achieve? Can he, as a Stakhanovite, even afford to go on strike? Would there be reprisals, would he jeopardise his career? Until now he had managed to survive without joining the Party, a delicate balancing act. But going on strike would be unequivocal. He recalled a saying from his Latin lessons at school: *Contra ventum non potest mingere*, you can't piss against the wind. He could not make up his mind. Then hearing reports on Radio Free Europe of thousands of people fleeing across the border from Hungary to Austria, he finally saw a possible solution to his dilemma.

On Saturday evening, the children in bed, he broached the subject with Mária. 'Swetheart, what if we escaped this whole awful mess here by walking over the border to Austria?'

Mária, taken by surprise mid-washing up, said after a long pause: 'What? You mean to *disszidál*?' She spat out the pejorative word from the Communist vocabulary that meant both to dissent and to defect.

'Yes, if that's what you want to call it. We could make a better life for ourselves away from here. Almost anywhere. Think about it, sweetheart!'

Mária did not like the idea at all, but could think of nothing but practical objections. 'How can we know if the border is still open? It would be very dangerous. What if we get shot at by the border guards? And isn't the border mined?'

Tamás tried to reassure her. 'They've cleared all the minefields. Even the actual, physical border is gone. The barbed wire was pulled down last May. Thousands of other people are leaving this way. I heard a lot of reassuring reports on Radio Free Europe. There's nothing to fear, sweetheart.'

'Still, it wouldn't be easy. I know what it's like.' Memories of those long-ago days, when she was fourteen, floated up in her mind. Fleeing from the Russians at the end of the war, with her parents and sister, from the east right across the whole country, until they were chased over the border to Austria.

'It was dreadful!' How can he not remember what she had told him? They had been so frightened, so cold, so hungry. 'This is the same time of year. We'll freeze!'

'Sweetheart, it will be totally different now. It's not the same situation. We can take warm clothes and everything we need.

Mária changed tack. 'But how would we manage to march across the freezing border carrying suitcases? With a four-year-old child and a twenty-month-old baby? It would be very traumatic for them. And irresponsible of us. No, no, it's simply impossible.'

'What if we left the children behind with your mother,' suggested Tamás, 'then later, once we've settled abroad, have them sent on after us by the Red Cross?'

'So you expect me to be separated not only from my mother but from my beloved babies? You want me to give them up, to abandon them?'

She was working herself up into a frenzy, her speech growing incoherent with emotion. 'You can't mean it! You can't! It's unbearable! I can't do it, I can't, I won't ...'

Finally, she managed to squeeze out what sounded like an ultimatum. 'If you want to leave, if that's what you really want, then go! ... But you go without me, ... and without the children!'

Tamás realised there was no way of convincing his wife.

Nothing resolved, they went to bed silently, turning away from each other, and their minds replayed the past hour – what was said, what was left unsaid, what should have been said – in endless loops until dawn came.

5

Family Life

The year after the revolution – or the 'failed counter-revolutionary uprising' according to the contemporary official designation – Mária and Tamás moved into a place of their own in Pest, on the other side of the Danube.

Since Tamás was not implicated in any of the events of the previous year, the widespread and brutal retributions that followed didn't affect them at all. He wasn't under investigation or on a blacklist, so when he applied for a flat, on the basis that the family have outgrown their one-room sublet in Buda, they were soon allocated one.

Their new flat was near the Eastern Railway Station, on the second floor of another turn-of-the-century block of flats, now owned and rented out by the district council. Before the war such a flat would have been home to a middle-class couple with a live-in maid, but in the new People's Republic it was considered suitable for a family of four.

Their road was the continuation of a busy avenue that radiated out from the Danube embankment. It started out as

Kossuth Street, changed into Rákóczi Road, before becoming Thököly Road – all its sections named after past political leaders who in various centuries fought in the cause of Hungarian independence. It gradually lost its smartness as it struggled eastwards and acquired an air of neglect by the time it reached the vicinity of the railway station. The area behind their block, surrounding a covered food market, had a reputation for night-time roughness and danger, reflected in its nickname of 'Little Chicago'.

Thököly Road was always jammed with buses and cars on both sides and trams running in the middle. In summer, when the windows had to be kept permanently open, the noise of daytime traffic and the conversations and footsteps of pedestrians at night ricocheted off the three-story-high façades as if in an urban canyon.

Their flat had two large, street-facing rooms. One became the living room-cum-bedroom for Mária and Tamás, who could finally sleep in their own space. The other was turned into the children's room, containing their divan beds and a table in the middle for homework and family lunches. The former 'maid's room' next to the kitchen became Tamás's workshop again.

Moving to Thököly Road represented a new stage in the family's life, a change from a constrained way of living to a more relaxed one. They had finally enough room for all their needs and they didn't have to share with anyone. Mária and Tamás bought a few pieces of furniture, they could invite friends round to play cards on a Sunday afternoon or have birthday parties for the children. The next autumn six-year old Rika started school, ten minutes' walk away, and Gábor followed in her footsteps three years later.

Mária wasn't keen on Rika and Gábor going out to play with other children in the grounds of the nearby City Park. 'I don't want you to mix with those rascals there', she said. She didn't encourage them to make friends at school either. The standard punishment she imposed on them for something they did or didn't do was to cancel the invitations to their classmates for play-dates or birthday parties.

The only playmate not censored by their mother was their cousin, Laci, a year older than Rika. But he and his mother, Aunt Blondie, didn't come over very often, even though the two sisters lived only a couple of Metro stops away from each other. Blondie's husband, Tibor, was not a sociable, friendly person – despite working in a personnel department – and he tried to keep his small family to itself, even disapproving of visits to and from his wife's relatives. He was also a harsh disciplinarian, laying down the law at home and beating his young son with his belt for even minor disobediences. As Blondie was fearful of the consequences for her son and dared not go against her husband's wishes, Rika and Gábor saw their frightened cousin very rarely.

Right from the beginning the relationship between Rika and Gábor was both combative and cooperative. After they got their own, though shared room, the early conflicts between them centred on the daily ritual of putting the toys away. One of them took on the role of the Gatherer, who had to bring to the shelf all the toys scattered on the floor during the day, and the other one became the Packer, putting the toys back onto the shelves.

The preferred roles changed daily and were noisily fought over every time.

Confined a lot to their room and to each other's company they invented their own simple games. *Smudgey* involved one player reflecting a light shape, the 'little smudge', onto a wall with a hand mirror and moving it fast in squiggly lines, while the other player would jump about, trying to 'catch it', hopelessly and hilariously.

Later, they made a theatre stage underneath the blanket covered dining table and acted out 'modern operas'. These consisted of singing gibberish, out-of-tune, while wearing a head-dress of a dishcloth under a colander crown.

Gábor admired his big sister, but this changed gradually as Rika demanded the last word in their arguments, claiming that because she was older 'she knew better'. The fights between them sometimes became physical and persisted until Gábor became stronger.

'Wait till your father comes home!' was Mária's customary reaction when the children did something naughty. It was a way of deferring the punishment and her attempt to involve Tamás more in the upbringing of their children. Often the threatened retributions did not come about, because Mária forgot to mention it or because Tamás came home late.

This time four-year-old Gábor had gone too far. Cooped up in the flat and bored on his own while Rika was at school, he started scribbling on anything he could lay his hands on, picture books or bedtime stories. Then he found a misshapen paper clip and discovered that he could make marks with that on surfaces that were impervious to his pencil. Imitating his sister he covered the wooden parts of the recently bought dining chairs with scratches and proudly showed the fruit of his labours to his mother, 'Anyu, look, I can write too.'

Back from work, Tamás was about to take his son to task when the phone rang and a friend asked for his help in repairing a radio. After suggesting a few diagnostic tricks, without success, he said into the receiver: 'Hang on for a minute, we'll try something else, but first I have to spank my son before his bedtime.' He laid the handset down.

Calling his son over, Tamás, seemingly bored by his assigned duty, asked: 'Now what is it that you have done, Gabi?'

'I scratched the chairs,' said Gábor in a small voice, barely audible.

'WHAT DID YOU DO?' roared his father.

Gábor repeated his previous answer in a playful singsong, almost defiantly, seeking complicity with his father. But it was no use.

'You know what the punishment for this is? Run out to the kitchen and bring me back a wooden spoon.'

Gábor, dawdling, half-fearing half-doubting the coming punishment, returned to the room, dragging the wooden spoon behind him like a toy.

'Pull your pants down!' commanded Tamás.

The child whimpered pleadingly.

His father repeated the order and added 'Lean forward!'

The sound of thwacking, followed by crying: 'Nooo, please Apu, nooooo!'

'If you don't shut up, you'll get more!' Then, as the sobs

gradually softened, 'There, you can pull your pants up. Are you going to do it again?'

A mumbled, inaudible reply.

'Well, are you? I can't hear you!'

Finally, a small voice breaking through the sniffles, 'I won't ...I won't... do it ... again.'

'All right. Now come and give me a kiss and take the wooden spoon back to the kitchen.'

As Gábor, still snivelling, left the room Tamás picked up the handset and returned to his remote radio repair. 'Now, where were we?'

Not long after moving to Thököly Road, Tamás left his factory job on Csepel island. He landed a position at the prestigious Telecommunications Research Institute, affiliated with the Academy of Sciences. A major bonus of his move was the yearly access to the Academy's holiday complex in a Balaton resort. A free fortnight stint in a workplace *üdülő* was a standard perk in socialist Hungary, a highlight of the year for families and an important safety valve from the regime's point of view.

The Academy's *üdülő* was on the southern shore of Lake Balaton, where the shallow water was ideal for families with young children. They spent the days at the lakeside beach area, next to the dormitory building, and there was a clubhouse, with a television and ping-pong and pool tables.

Full board was provided in the restaurant building. Tamás and Mária, not normally drinkers, ordered wine with lunch and dinner, and the bottle marked with their name and the level of the liquid in it was taken back to the kitchen after the meal and brought out at the next time. When the children woke up from their afternoon nap they had cold milky coffee and butter-and-honey sandwiches on the veranda of the restaurant.

In the evenings Mária and Tamás would leave the children in the care of a babysitter, the daughter of a fellow holidaymaker, and go off to the clubhouse to watch television, to play cards or to dance. The music – Fats Domino, Little Richard or Chuck Berry – was supplied by Tamás on his portable reel-to-reel tape recorder. Sometimes Gábor would wake up and want his mummy, and the babysitter would bundle up the crying, unpacifiable child and carry him to his parents.

The place became the habitual scene of their two-week-long summer vacations. This was where Rika taught herself to swim by throwing her lifesaver ahead and swimming-crawling after it in water barely up to her waist. It was here that five-year-old Gábor slipped on the mossy wooden steps and fell headlong into the shallows, after which even his father could not entice him back into the water for the rest of that holiday. In later years bikes were hired for the children and they could roam freely in the resort, which they weren't allowed to do in Budapest.

Every year after the school-year had finished in mid-June and before going on holiday in July two things would happen. First, for a few days Rika and Gábor's room became a tailor's atelier. Mária engaged a seamstress and with her help she made summer clothes – frocks for herself and Rika, shirts and shorts for Gábor. Nothing for Tamás, though, because having no interest whatsoever in clothes he was not dissatisfied with the meagre selection in the shops. But Mária liked to dress nicely, vaguely keeping an eye on the current fashion, and the children needed yearly replacements of things they have grown out of, so home dressmaking was a quality as well as a frugal solution.

Mária, who'd learnt to make clothes at secondary school, took the measurements and drew up the patterns herself. After the pieces were cut out and temporarily assembled, Rika and Gábor had to try on the emerging garments, carefully, so as not to dislodge the sewing pins. Then their mother, with more pins clamped between her lips, adjusted a shoulder or took in a side or attached the sleeves. Gábor hated it all; he squirmed, he couldn't stand still, he complained about being pricked by the pins. But Rika enjoyed the performance of climbing up onto the table and turning slowly around while her mother pinned the hem of her skirt. The seamstress did the fitting of the clothes being made for Mária, as well as doing all the machining on the old treadle-operated Singer, before joining her client in the hand-finishing of the garments.

The second thing, and essential during their long absence from the flat, was organising DIY pest control. Before the war the building they lived in on Thököly Road housed a wholesale grocery business and the food that was stored on its premises had given rise to an enduring infestation of cockroaches. On the last morning, just before the family's departure for the Balaton, Tamás would push the furniture to the middle of the rooms and cover the parquet floor along the walls with DDT. Two weeks later they would come back to the shuttered up flat and find every white-dusted surface littered with dead roaches. They would throw open the windows and sweep up the carcases, and would be free of cockroaches for a few short months, before certain noises at night and scurrying insects on the floor in sudden lamplight would reveal the return of the intrusion.

Rika was in bed with a high temperature and a splitting ear-ache. She had a middle ear infection, brought on by catching a cold, occurring at least once each winter. Her mother gave her a Kalmopyrin to bring down the fever and briskly applied a wet-and-warm compress to the painful left ear. Then she disappeared into the kitchen to make her daughter a slice of buttered bread crowned by a thin veil of salami – convalescent food, normally judged too costly. Rika fell into a feverish sleep and when she woke up she found her grandmother perched on the edge of her bed.

Granny Katus often stayed with them at Thököly Road, when Rika had an attack of her recurring ear problem. Although Katus didn't have the warmest relationship with her daughter-in-law, at these times she felt Mária welcomed her help. She sat with her granddaughter for hours, reading her stories, trying to provide a distraction from the pain. It was thanks to her that Rika had learnt to read and write before she started school, so despite being frequently sick in the first couple of years, she did not fall behind.

Rika's earaches were slow to clear and when the steam-pack home treatment did not work, the solution was either penicillin injections or the piercing of the eardrum. Luckily, there was a paediatrician who had his home and private practice on the floor below theirs, and they went to him for emergency consultations.

Having a doctor living in the same building proved ultimately life saving. One winter Rika's ear infection was accompanied by dangerously high fever. After a quick examination the doctor rushed her to the hospital in his own car, fearing that any delay could result in sepsis for the little girl. On arrival Rika was taken to the operating theatre immediately to have an infected bone behind her ear removed. The crisis was averted. Fortunately her hearing was not affected and after this operation the frequency of her ear problems tapered off.

Tamás and Mária often remarked that treatments of Rika's illnesses had cost them the equivalent of a Mercedes. Their jokey but much repeated comments had two consequences. Gábor registered this as a demonstration of him being less valued and valuable, as he only cost his parents a Trabant. Rika, on the other hand, felt that the frequent references to what her parents had spent on her was meant to make her feel guilty and obedient in return.

While Tamás and Mária would not have admitted a preference for either of their children, the two grandmothers had no such scruples. Granny Katus liked Rika better because she herself had sons and in a lucky symmetry Granny Lizi, who had daughters, had a soft spot for Gábor.

Rika's closeness to her 'own' grandmother was the most likely reason that her first communion was witnessed not by regular churchgoer Lizi, nor by Rika's godmother, Blondie, but by practically atheist Katus.

It was Mária who insisted that Rika should take part in this ceremony, not so much out of strong faith, more out of keeping with conventions. Aunt Blondie would simply discharge her godmother-duties by asking Rika from time to time: 'Have you been to church? ... Have you been to confession?' Tamás treated the occasion of his daughter's first communion as a photo opportunity. He took endless shots inside the church of six-year-old Rika in her white dress, gloves and veil; in the procession with other young girls carrying candles and flowers; afterwards at a *cukrászda* celebrating with cakes, and at home in numerous compositions of parents, children and Granny Katus.

One Christmas Katus made Rika an unusual gift. Being short of money, she bought a cheap plastic doll and made for it a set of clothes, hand-stitched and scaled-down versions of what a girl of Rika's age would wear.

Rika and Gábor, dressed up in their best clothes, were waiting impatiently in their room on Christmas Eve. They had not been allowed into their parents' room, where the adults were decorating the tree all afternoon. At last they'd heard the tinkling of the little bell and rushed in to see what 'little Jesus' brought them.

'Wait a bit, Marikám, we have to light the candles first,' said Mária to her daughter.

Granny Lizi gently held Gábor in front of her by the shoulders to prevent him springing forward.

Tamás put on a record of a Christmas song and they all sang along with it. *Stille Nacht! Heilige Nacht!*

When at last she was allowed to look, Rika found under the tree a pretty doll and a rectangular box, which turned out to contain the doll's wardrobe. It was made of cardboard, with properly closing doors and inside hung miniature clothes on small hangers. There was a dark blue pleated skirt to go with a white blouse, a protective apron to wear on top and a hooded, red duvetyne duffel coat with shiny black lining and tiny toggles. Rika squeaked with delight when she discovered that the doll even had underwear and a pale pink nightdress made from some silky material.

Rika loved her present. It was made for her and nobody had anything like it. She felt special. How clever her grandmother was, creating something out of so little – a few scraps of fabric, a shoe-box, some bits of wood. Something she actually liked, not boring practical presents like a warm winter scarf. She could not be separated from her doll during the holiday, even taking it to her bed in its pink nightdress.

A few days later, when she went back to school, boisterous little brother Gábor cracked the head of the doll. Rika was in tears and asked her parents if they could get her another doll. They promised, and she waited and waited. In the end she never got one and before long she grew out of dolls. But she cherished the tiny clothes and the little wardrobe for a long time.

A year after Rika's ear operation it was decided, on currently prevailing medical advice, that both children should have their tonsils removed to prevent recurring infections. They were kept in hospital for a few days on separate wards, with very short visiting times. For Gábor, a cheerful little boy of five, the feeling of having been abandoned added to the trauma of the operation. What made matters worse was that the medical practice of the time required that the little patients be given crusts of bread to eat as soon as possible, supposedly to aid wound healing.

The pain put Gábor off his food for a long time and he had to be cajoled into eating at every meal. So much so that at the home of the childminder, a grandmotherly figure who looked after a handful of pre-school children in her own flat, even the parrot learnt the coaxing, pleading words, repeated at every lunchtime: 'Gabika, have a little more! Gabika, eat a bit more!'

But the encouragement was not very effective and during the course of a year Gábor had changed from a chubby little boy to a thin one.

Rika was doing well at school right from the start, getting top grades in most subjects every semester. This created a persisting expectation so that when she occasionally got a 'Good' mark instead of an 'Excellent' in drawing or physical education or singing, her mother regarded it as a minor disgrace.

In her third year at school the topic for eight-year-old Rika's composition homework was *What I did yesterday*. She enjoyed writing it and when she got her work back from the teacher with a 'Well done' remark, she showed the piece to her mother.

She was especially proud of the last sentence: *After my father had returned from work, the whole family set down to eat together and we consumed with relish the tasty potato soup left over from lunch.* Rika was watching her mother's face while she was reading it and was looking forward to her approval.

When she finished, however, Mária didn't praise her daughter; on the contrary, she berated her. 'How can you write such a thing! Now people will think we're so poor that we only have potatoes to eat.'

'But that's what happened, that's what we ate yesterday when Apu got home,' protested Rika.

'You don't have to tell everybody! I'm so ashamed.'

'But I also wrote that it tasted good and we enjoyed it.'

'Eating leftovers ... How can I look people in the eye now? They will think I don't cook something fresh for every meal.' Mária was very upset and it took long before she calmed down.

After this incident Rika had to show her mother every composition before handing it in.

As Tamás was an electrical engineer, everybody assumed that the family would have the latest electrical equipment at home. But his attitude was, 'Why should I buy something when I know how to make it?' Except that he was not in a hurry, in Mária's view too lazy, to make things for the family.

At first he knocked up radios that were put together from the necessary parts and just about fulfilled their functions, but looked like ongoing learning projects rather than their commercial counterparts. After starting school Gábor became interested in what his father was doing in his den and Tamás initiated his son into all things electronic. When father and son successfully assembled one transistor radio – capacitors, diodes and transistors soldered onto a base board – it was taken apart after a few days and they set out to build a more complicated one, before that one in turn was cannibalised and re-made into an improved version.

They had no television either long after other families had already bought theirs. After a lot of nagging by his wife Tamás finally constructed one, from a cathode-ray tube and other components he came across – he would say, liberated – in his work. The home-built TV stood in the corner of the living room looking unfinished, with wires hanging out and no back cover. When it sporadically stopped working they had to bang on its side to get it going again and the capricious TV-top antenna needed constant adjustments.

After her ninth birthday one of Rika's Christmas presents was a year's subscription to books. They came in the post, proper grown-up looking volumes, in a differently coloured cloth cover each month. Classic Hungarian novels, swashbuckling, romantic or historical, mostly from the nineteenth century. She would look out for the postman, then crouching on a low stool with her back to the ceramic stove greedily devour her latest treasure in two-three days and wait impatiently for the next one.

The following year the selection changed to world literature, introducing Rika and, with a couple of years' delay, Gábor to the world of Ivanhoe, the Count of Monte Cristo, Captain Nemo or the tales of Shakespeare. As their imaginations were fired up they found nothing strange in the fact that in these books not only the language was translated, but the writers and the characters appeared to be Hungarian: Dickens Károly and Verne Gyula, or Copperfield Dávid and Twist Olivér.

These novels lay the foundation of the children's reading habits and, in the absence of a working TV or being allowed to see friends from school, books became their main source of entertainment at home. Having exhausted the supply of the family bookcase Rika made regular fortnightly visits to the local library, returning every time with the maximum number of volumes she could borrow. After finishing a novel she would carry on under its spell, behaving as the heroine would and imitating her speech and mannerism. When Gábor moved on from the books that arrived in the post, his preference was first for adventure stories about Apache and Sioux Indians, before precociously getting into science fiction via Verne Gyula and H. G. Wells.

6

Grandparents and Holidays

One Saturday morning in January Rika got on the tram next to the Eastern Railway station on the way to visit her grandmother. After the operation had put an end to Rika's recurring ear-infections, Granny Katus hardly ever came to see them at Thököly Road. Her mother said it was because Granny was getting old and frail and finding it difficult, but Rika sensed that her mother and her father's mother didn't like each other much. If she wanted to spend time with her grandmother she had to go to Kőbánya. And now that she was ten she was allowed to travel on her own.

Despite being bundled up in a three-sizes-too-big-you'll-grow-into-it sheepskin coat, with knitted hat, scarf and gloves, she was shivering. It was freezing in the open platform trams and she had to change a couple times. She was relieved when the small chapel on a raised ground came into view. This was the landmark for the final stop of the last tram she had to take. From here it was still a lengthy walk down the unfriendly street past the big red-brick church, but at least she would warm up a little.

The district where Granny Katus and Grandpa József lived was semi-industrial. Their neighbours were a pharmaceutical factory, assembly workshops and a high rise hostel for workers from outside Budapest. The railway lines in and out of the capital ran beyond the main road and the rattling of trains rumbling past at all hours became embedded in people's consciousness. There were no shops nearby or anything else that may have made life a little easier or more pleasant for people living in the area.

Most of the houses were single-story buildings. Rika's grandparents occupied one of the middle flats of a terraced row of five, fronted by a narrow strip of communal garden. Their flat consisted of nothing more than a kitchen, a single room and an indoor toilet, all opening from a small hall.

When Rika finally arrived after her long journey, Granny Katus heated up some water on the stove and tried to unthaw her granddaughter's numb hands and feet in a basin of warm water. Grandpa József was out, the smell of tobacco and alcohol deputising for his presence, as usual.

They sat in the kitchen, warmed by the heat from the oven. Granny Katus was knitting something in austere grey and Rika read aloud from a collection of her grandmother's favourite Petőfi poems. She didn't in fact need the book. She had recited these poems so many times that she already knew them by heart. *The garden flowers still blossom in the vale / Before our house the poplars are still green / But soon the mighty winter will prevail / Snow is already in the mountain seen.*

By midday the lentil soup Granny Katus had bubbling on the stove was ready and they could have their lunch, but

Grandpa hadn't yet returned. They waited for him for a while, Rika munching on a heel of bread to blunt her hunger, but in the end they ate without him. He still hadn't come back before Rika had to leave in the early afternoon to get home before dark. She never stayed overnight as there was nowhere for her to sleep.

The next day they received the news that Grandpa József had collapsed on the street and died, apparently of a heart attack. Three weeks later when his funeral took place the children were not taken along to the cemetery because Mária didn't want them to miss school. As Grandpa József had only minimally been part of Rika and Gábor's life until then, his permanent disappearance from it afterwards hardly registered with them, especially because they had not witnessed his burial.

After her husband's death, Granny Katus, in her early sixties and suffering from pernicious anaemia, went to live with her younger son, Pál. Rika's visits to her 'own' grandmother came to an abrupt stop, because her mother said she was too young to travel on her own that far across the river.

Even though Uncle Pál was nominally Gábor's godfather, Tamás's relationship with his brother was not close. They didn't see each other very often, especially after Pál married the daughter of a renowned writer and bought a flat on classy Gellért Hill in Buda. Although Tamás was just as much at fault in not maintaining closer links between their two families, he blamed his brother's intellectual snobbery for the distance that had grown between them. And it resulted in Granny Katus vanishing from her grandchildren's life for some time.

During the summers Rika and Gábor would spend the bulk of

the two-and-a-half-month-long school holidays at their mother's parents.

Albertfalva, where Granny Lizi and Grandpa László lived, was a leafy garden suburb in southern Buda. Their house was at the end of the bus route, the last stop conveniently in front of the gate, but there was hardly any other traffic on the wide, tree-lined streets. Their one-room flat was not much larger than Granny Katus's, but they had a proper bathroom and a vine-shaded strip of a terrace leading to a small garden, which they shared with their upstairs neighbour. In their only room the flexible sitting-sleeping furniture could put all three grandchildren up, if needed, the extending table could accommodate large family gatherings, and they even managed to find room for a piano, a remnant of a middle-class life of another age.

On mornings that promised a hot day Lizi put a large tin bath tub out onto the terrace, filled it with buckets of tap water, and once it warmed up from the sun the children splashed and frolicked in their makeshift pool and Gábor raced toy ships tied to the legs of frogs.

The small garden had a cherry and a quince tree, providing cooling shade in the summer heat to the adults, and climbing and fruit guzzling fun for the children. The next door neighbour, a retired postman, drenched the gardens every evening with a hosepipe and after the daily watering Gábor collected the frogs that emerged in the damp shade. One day this neighbour Uncle played a trick on six-year-old Gábor: he suggested putting the frogs to sleep with some gas-like substance he had. Only when the frogs didn't wake up the following morning did Gábor realise that he had helped killing them and was very upset.

Going to stay in Albertfalva was always fun and full of treats for the children. They were often taken to the small local cinema by Granny Lizi. She didn't like the serious, ideology-heavy Hungarian films of the times and preferred foreign comedies or musicals on screen. These products from the West only made it past the censors if they were judged politically innocuous and were usually shown years after their original releases. So the children chuckled through the adventures of Norman Wisdom's Pitkin – an acceptable working class hero fighting the capitalist system – or hummed along to musical biopics with Mario Lanza as the poor fisherman becoming a celebrated singer.

Once Granny Lizi took her granddaughter to see Swan Lake, after which nine-year-old Rika leaped and pirouetted around the room in front of her grandmother's visiting friend, bumping into furniture, upsetting cakes and coffee cups, pretending to be a ballerina in her clumsy swan-imitation.

In the early 1960s when the craze for the twist reached Hungary – trends from abroad always got delayed, like black polo-necks coming into fashion in Budapest during the dog days of summer – it was at her grandparents' place that Rika practised her moves in front of the wardrobe mirror, grinding out a non-existent cigarette end with her foot and drying her back with an imaginary towel.

After finishing the daily cooking and housework, in the afternoons Granny Lizi would change from her unflattering work clothes into a more presentable house-coat, sit down at the piano and play what she remembered from her lessons when she was a young girl. She would have liked her grandchildren to take up a musical instrument seriously, but none of them was keen on lessons or regular practice. Rika and Gábor just wanted to mess about on the piano to while away the time at their grandparents and they taught themselves easy, basic tunes, played with one finger. Later on they 'composed' protest songs with their own lyrics, which were born out of their own rebellious spirit but were also influenced, more than a little, by the propaganda they heard at school: *Brave Vietnam, do not give up / Brave Vietnam, keep holding out / Look how the French / At Dien Bien Phu / In the end they all bit the dust.*

Rika and Gábor found the old-fashioned world of their grandparents fascinating and endearing.

In the years before Granny Lizi could afford a fridge, keeping food from going off in the summer heat called for well-thought-out traditional solutions. She had a tin-lined, wooden ice box, the size of a small cupboard. The ice was delivered by a horse-drawn cart, the seller ringing his bell as he was trundling through the streets and then cutting off chunks with an ice-saw to the lengths the housewives required. Gábor always listened out for the ice-seller's bell and dragged his Granny outside, so he could pat the horse and feed it sugar cubes while she bought the ice. Once the ice was put into the box, the limited space remaining in it was saved for expensive foodstuff like meat, so other ways of preserving food also had to be employed.

When they bought milk, which was ladled into their own tin can in the shop, it had to be boiled straight after it was carried home, then allowed to cool down, before it could be stored for a day or two on the cold, tiled floor of the north-facing pantry. But Granny Lizi would often allow some of the milk to turn into *aludttej,* as this spontaneously fermenting, home-made yoghurt was everyone's favourite summer breakfast.

Granny Lizi had a younger brother, a doctor, who left Hungary in 1949 and ended up in Brazil, where he married a local woman. From there he regularly sent parcels to his sisters, with items that he believed would make their lives easier. When a parcel arrived the recipient had to pay import duty on it before they were allowed to take it home and discover what was inside.

Often Granny Lizi got lengths of expensive fabrics, from which she had a local dressmaker make her smart dresses. Sometimes she received fashionable clothes, belated copies of the New Look, but suitable for slim, young women only, so she passed them on to her daughters, who shone in these taffeta creations at New Year's Eve parties. Once she got a fur stole, complete with the dangling feet of some animal, which became part of Rika's costume, teamed with a brown cardigan and baggy corduroy trousers, when she played a fox in a school play.

Occasionally the contents of the parcels were baffling. There was an outfit that someone must have got for the Rio carnival: a flower-patterned dress with a fitted bodice and a full, floor-sweeping skirt, a straw hat and a parasol. Something Scarlett O'Hara might have worn, but not very useful in Socialist Hungary, so it remained in the dressing-up box among clothes that Rika would prance around in at her grandmother's. Yet another of the impractical items, a sequinned tulle gown, was made into an odalisque costume by Mária for her ten-year-old daughter to wear at a fancy dress competition at school. Rika not only didn't win, but her get-up was officially denounced as 'remnant of a petty bourgeois mindset', and the competition was won by Popeye the Sailor, a proper representative of the working class.

While staying in Albertfalva the children were usually taken to church on Sundays. For Granny Lizi these were mostly social occasions and she would dress up for them in the latest outfit created from the parcels her brother had sent. But she did not always go with them to mass, because she was not feeling well or was cooking something elaborate for lunch. At these times she instructed the children to bring their grandfather back straight from the church, without any detours.

'Your Grandpa cannot have a drink, because of his war injury. The doctors said that even a spritzer could cause a blackout and may kill him. So don't let him go to the *kocsma*, steer him away, come back by the other route.'

After László and Lizi got married and while their daughters were small, László scrupulously heeded the prohibition and never touched alcohol. Years later, though, when the doctors' fatal prediction had not come true and he was not under his wife's watchful eyes, he would come back from any outing via the *kocsma*. When Lizi inevitably found out his misstep, he was always ready with his pleading explanation: 'But my throat was so thirsty!'

Following his retirement the only other chances Grandpa László got to quench his permanent thirst were his once-a-week casual night-shifts at the Lottery organisers. He took advantage of all these opportunities, but his small rebellions sometimes did result in him loosing consciousness and having to be brought home by strangers.

It was a name-day celebration for Granny Lizi. The whole family, Mária's and her sister Blondie's, gathered in Albertfalva, six adults and three children crammed in around the table for Sunday lunch.

Having finished his meal Tamás, pleading tiredness as usual, was about to settle down for a nap behind the backs of the adults sitting on the divan-bed. The conversation continued around him. His head already on a cushion and his shod feet dangling off the edge of the divan, he asked his daughter, 'Marikám, would you do something for me?'

Rika – who was only ever called 'Marikám' at Christmas or when she was asked to do something she didn't want to do – knew what was coming and played for time. 'Apu, I haven't finished … I'm still eating.'

'You're almost finished, hurry up with it.'

Then, a couple of minutes later, 'Marikám, would you take my shoes off for me, I would be much more comfortable without them.'

'Apu, you know I don't like to do it, I don't like …' She wrinkled her nose while pointing with it at her father's feet.

Tamás went on the offensive, 'Are you saying my feet are smelly?'

Rika wanted to answer, yes, and everybody knows how much I hate doing it. But she was unable to utter those words, didn't know why. She said, 'No, no, it's just … it's …,' and looked at her mother and the other adults for help.

No one came to her rescue. After slowly swallowing the last mouthful of her lunch and with it her excuse for the delay, she capitulated again to her father. She got up from her seat and skirting the table went over to him. Then she unlaced his shoes, took them off and carried the pair in one hand, holding her nose with the other, to the furthest corner of the room.

The adults around the table, half-listening half-ignoring the father-daughter interaction, went on with their after lunch chat, which was soon accompanied by snores behind their back. Lizi bit her tongue, not wanting to start an argument with her son-in-law. There was nothing that could jolt her husband, László, out of his placid habit of non-involvement. Blondie and her husband didn't think it was their business to comment.

Mária was upset, feeling that her husband's behaviour was rude and disrespectful towards her parents and her family. She did not say anything either, so as not to spoil the occasion, but resolved to mention it to him later.

By 1963 Tamás was doing well enough in his job at the Research Institute to be able to buy a car. He suggested driving to the Romanian seaside for their annual holiday, instead of staying as usual by the Balaton, the 'Hungarian sea'. The preparation for the vacation involved getting red passports, which entitled them and their children for unlimited travel in other socialist countries.

The Škoda was packed to overflowing with everything imaginable for the holiday, including the customary wand of salami. They set off at dawn to beat the mid-July heat. The children, eight-and-a-half and not-yet-eleven, started out excited, then grew bored on the journey, then became nauseous from the smell of the Romanian petrol seeping into the back of the car. To break up the long drive Tamás and Mária planned to stop for a few nights in Kolozsvár to visit Mária's aunt, her father's sister, who still lived there.

Crossing the border triggered in Mária recollections of her family's history, and an urge to tell. Partly for Tamás and partly as an explanation for the children.

'My father, Grandpa László,' – Mária turned towards the children in the back seat – 'was born in Kolozsvár and he left the town at seventeen when he enlisted from school and went off to war. Then, after Trianon, his birthplace become part of Romania and he settled down in 'truncated' Hungary.'

'Didn't you also live in Kolozsvár? When was that?' Tamás vaguely remembered being told about this when they first met.

'Yes, when this part of Transylvania was returned to Hungary, my father insisted we move back to the place where he was from. I was only about ten. We spent four years here and although the war was going on, it was far away, it didn't really affect our lives. That is until the Russians came and we had to flee.'

Mária expected her husband or the children to ask about what happened next, but Tamás was concentrating on his driving on unfamiliar roads and Rika and Gábor were more interested in playing 'I spy'. They were also approaching their stop-over destination, so she didn't continue with her reminiscences.

As Tamás was driving through the centre of Kolozsvár,

Mária tried to find traces of her rosy memories of living here as a young girl. The house where they lived, the convent school she and her sister attended, the Lido where they went swimming – some recognisable places or corners. But there had been so much re-building in the past almost twenty years, the streets and squares all re-named in Romanian, she found it impossible to identify anything.

Aunt Ilona and Uncle Feri's house was on the outskirts of the town, on a street with open ditches for rainwater and village-style peasant houses at right angles to the street, like the teeth of a comb. The main gate from the street led to a long, rectangular yard and from there, under an arched porch, you entered the rooms of the house. There was the main or 'clean' room, with windows overlooking the street, where they slept and entertained visitors, connecting with the kitchen, the scene of most daytime activities, then the pantry and the workshop, and lastly what was once the barn, with the hay-store overhead. At the back of the yard was the vegetable patch, next to the privy.

The whole household was permeated by the smell of tarragon: small sachets of the dried herb scented clothes and bedlinen; steeped in vinegar it flavoured vegetable dishes and long-simmered stews, while perfuming the kitchen; and bunches of the dried herb were hung under the eaves for keeping away insects.

There were not enough beds in the house for everyone, so long wooden pallets with mattresses of crackling, sweet-smelling straw were set up for Rika and Gábor in the barn. The novelty of it all was so thrilling, so much better than their usual summer holidays, a real adventure. But soon the nocturnal sounds of the bats, mice and owls turned frightening for these two city children. First Gábor ran in crying, then Mária came out to rescue her daughter from sleeping alone. They all slept together and late, in the big double bed and by the morning all was forgotten, at least by the children.

It was already hot, coming up to the midday bells. Aunt Ilona had cooked a celebratory lunch, and invited her son and daughter-in-law along for a family get-together. The men dragged out the heavy table from the kitchen and set it up under the dappled shade of the walnut tree. Going in and out, from kitchen to yard, carrying plates, cutlery and glasses for eight people, Rika was hit every time by the smell of tarragon. The garden bench and various chairs from the house were mustered, wine was brought up from the cellar, and *pálinka* from the cupboard. Aunt Ilona carried the china tureen to the table and started to ladle out the fragrant chicken soup. Uncle Feri stopped her: 'Wait, we have to drink a toast first!' and poured out shots of *pálinka*. The children had clinked their glasses with *málnaszörp* – home-made raspberry cordial with splashes of water from the soda syphon. 'Wait, let's have a photo together!' called out Tamás, running to his parked car for the camera.

After the lunch with wiener schnitzel and numerous toasts of red wine, rounded up by dessert with their own walnut liqueur, there was no chance of going anywhere, so further travelling was postponed till the following morning. As they were going to leave at dawn, Aunt Ilona packed a hamper basket for the journey, with smoked sausages and a big round country bread, made with potatoes to stop it drying out.

In order to save the cost of an overnight stay Tamás drove for over ten hours non-stop before they reached the Black Sea just as night was falling.

They rented a room for a week in the house of a local family outside Mamaia and drove to the free beach every day, armed with lilos, camping beds and home-made windbreaks.

Mária prepared their food every day in their hosts' kitchen, muttering under her breath that a self-catering vacation was no vacation for her.

Rika made friends with the daughter of the family they stayed with, as only pre-teen girls with no shared language can.

Gábor tried to get his father to join him in building sandcastles on the beach, but Tamás only wanted to sleep and rest on his annual break.

In retrospect the summer was memorable not so much for their first experience of a foreign, seaside holiday, but for that dreamy, tarragon suffused stopover in Kolozsvár. The last holiday they had together as a family before everything unravelled.

7

A Phone Call and Consequences

The phone call came mid-afternoon. The children were in their room doing homework. Mária ran to the hall, answered the telephone and had a brief conversation. When she returned to the kitchen she was struggling to compose her face while she counted out the money for Aunty Hilda, who came to help with the weekly wash.

'Goodbye! Would *Nagyságos Asszony* like me to come the same time next Monday?' Aunty Hilda, putting on her coat, asked this question every week. She was a long-standing friend of the family, regarded almost as a third grandmother to the children, and often included in photos taken at events like first communions. Yet she called Mária by the outdated, formal title used by domestic servants in the old days. Mária had never protested against being addressed as Madam or suggested something more familiar.

Mária closed the door after Aunty Hilda and sank down on a kitchen stool. Her daily life, revolving around home and family, was suddenly replaying before her eyes. The monotonous pattern of Tamás leaving for work and the children for school, her shopping in the covered market behind their block, then housework and cooking lunch to be ready when Rika and Gábor came home. Ironing and mending clothes in the afternoon, then waiting for Tamás to return after working late. The joyless cavalcade of routine.

The phone call had been from Uncle Jon, an older colleague of her husband. He thought she should know that Tamás had been seen going into nightclubs with women.

At first Mária was tempted to dismiss this as malicious gossip. But Uncle Jon had always been kind to her when they met at events organised by Tamás's workplace, like the May Day Parade last year. Surely, he had no reason to make things up. Besides, it only confirmed her suspicions. She could no longer ignore the signs – Tamás had not been around much with the family, always coming home late from work and going on a good many weekend 'field trips' recently.

His behaviour last winter fitted into the picture too. When they were housed in that emergency place, while the collapsed floor of their flat in Thököly Road was being rebuilt. He had hardly ever been there, he had left her to cope. She and the children carried buckets of coal from the merchant two blocks away, through the snowy streets, up two flights of clanking metal stairs, to feed the small iron stove, which was not up to the task of keeping the place warm. The water froze overnight in the washbasin. And how he still tried to persuade her to have a third child. Was it to rescue their marriage? Or to keep her tied down while he pursued his own amusements away from home?

The dread of the future was spiralling through her mind: being on her own, without a man, without status or social approval, a woman deserted by her husband, becoming a single parent, the shame of being divorced. People pitying her.

Her thoughts flew back to her late teens and to the group of young men buzzing around her. Tall, broad shouldered and suntanned, handsome as matinee idols. Then on holiday by the Balaton meeting Tamás, who, smitten by her, swiftly gave up his girlfriend and joined the group of Mária's admirers. Already slightly balding, he couldn't compete in looks with her other suitors, but he swept her off her feet and she fell in love with him. Was she wrong in her choice? Should she have listened to her mother?

Then another image. In hot, sultry, high summer she was walking with Tamás under the plane trees on Margit Island. She had finished school and been taking singing lessons. She was talking excitedly about her audition the next day, where it might lead, how she hoped one day to have a career as a singer. She sensed that Tamás was less enthusiastic about her plans, so when he suggested having an ice cream she agreed to it to placate him, despite thinking it was not the most sensible thing to have before a singing test. The next day her throat was scratchy and inflamed, her voice croaky and she missed her chance. That was the end of her dreams.

Rika was awakened by sounds coming from the next room. The faint strip of light under the interconnecting double doors signalled that her father had come home. Her parents were having a not always whispered row in the marital bed. Nothing unusual in this, except the intensity. This latest quarrel seemed to have something to do with the afternoon's phone call. While doing her homework she overheard through the half-open door her mother's side of the conversation in the hall. At the time Rika couldn't work out what had happened, but now the pieces were coming together.

In the dim light seeping into the room shared with her brother she could see Gábor asleep, undisturbed, and she envied him. She tried to go back to sleep by putting the little pillow over her ear, but could not block out the sounds completely. Her parents' voices ebbed and flowed, fading out and in. *I've met the love of my life ... what about me? ... I don't want to miss this chance of a lifetime ... your duty as a husband ... I've never felt like this in my life ... abandoning your family ... have you thought about the children? ... I would like to think it over ... it will devastate them ... after 12 years of marriage ... I can't decide ... the right thing to do ... you'd better leave at once ...*

Rika had eventually drifted off on the wave of voices. By next morning her father was gone. Back from school that day, she and Gábor found that the room they'd called their own had been emptied out and their beds squeezed into what was previously their parents' room. From now on this became the scene of all their everyday activities. All three of them slept there and preparing for bed each evening turned into a tearful activity for their mother.

And next door the unheated room with the solitary camping bed was kept ready and waiting for when their father might come back and want to sleep there. A constant reminder of something broken and shameful.

Tamás came by the flat a few days later to pick up some clothes and told Mária that he had moved into his mother's place in Kőbánya, which had been empty for months after Katus had gone to live with her younger son following the death of her husband. Mária was incensed. How could Katus allow her son the use of her flat? It amounted to condoning his behaviour and his desertion of his family. She had never had a close relationship with her mother-in-law, but now she decided not to contact her any more, assuming Katus would take her son's side.

Initially Maria didn't want anybody to know that Tamás had moved out, even if it later proved temporary. What would people think? How could she bear the shame? She hoped he would come to his senses, realise where his responsibilities lie and return. And then, nobody would need to know what had gone on. As if it had never happened.

Her hopes of a quick reconciliation fading after a few of weeks, Mária felt a growing need to confide to somebody in her family. When her mother rang one morning, she blurted out without thinking: 'Tamás's left me'.

Calling from a public payphone Lizi was on the point of cursing Tamás, when she noticed her neighbour queuing up behind her. Not wanting to provide a topic for local gossip, she said to her daughter, 'I'm coming over straight away', and ended her call.

From then on every week Lizi came over from Albertfalva and spent a day at Thököly Road. Her visits were at first for moral support, then became necessary practical help after Mária had got a job and gone out to work.

Rika and Gábor loved their grandmother's visits. Arriving back from school they would be welcomed by the sweet buttery smell of Kugelhopf or walnut-dusted pull-apart cake. They also liked what she made for them for lunch, quite different from their mother's cooking. Before coming over to Thököly Road Lizi would queue up at her local butcher's who saved for her the cheapest cuts – tripe or kidney or brain – and she cooked such lip-smackingly tasty stews that the children always looked forward to 'Granny's day'.

But they hated how the afternoons usually ended. After lunch Granny Lizi, her hands occupied by darning socks, would sooner or later launch into her monologue.

'I've never liked your father. But your grandfather wanted to give him the benefit of the doubt, when he started courting your mother. She had such eligible young men after her, but she had to fall in love with your father... I warned her, but she wouldn't listen.'

'I saw his faults, he was so full of himself ...' Grandma, warming to her subject, continued. 'He couldn't be trusted. He had ditched his previous lady-friend, just before starting to chase after your mother. He had a roving eye, it was obvious.'

The week after President Kennedy's assassination they hoped the shocking news would provide a distraction to their grandmother. But after briefly commenting, 'Such a young and handsome man. Why would anybody want to harm him?' she reverted to her favourite topic. 'What kind of a woman takes up with a married man? A floozy, that's who. But, mark my word, it won't end well. His fancy woman will lead him a merry dance. God will make sure your father will get what he deserves. The mills of the gods grind slowly...!'

Rika and Gábor tried but never succeeded in diverting Granny Lizi from her verbal thrashing of their father or from calling down biblical punishments on his head. They were always relieved when at long last they heard their mother's key in the door.

After Tamás had left, Mária cried herself to sleep every night, pulling the duvet over her head, so the children, sleeping in the same room, wouldn't hear. Otherwise she went about her daily routine as before, keeping up a front in public. The passing of time was marked by her mother's weekly 'I told you so' sermons or some money from Tamás arriving by post every month. She waited for something to change, for the nightmare to go away.

When several months elapsed without hearing from Tamás, Mária filed for divorce. She felt badly treated and her wounded pride could not bear waiting any longer for Tamás to decide if he wanted to pursue the 'love of his life' or wanted to stay with her and the children. This uncertainty of living in limbo had to be changed, one way or another.

Within a few days and the first time since Tamás had moved out, Katus rang Mária. She had just heard her son's side of the story and blamed her daughter-in-law for not trying to save the marriage.

'Why don't you withdraw the petition?' Katus said. 'The whole thing may blow over soon. You know what men are like, Tamás will get over this infatuation. He will come back. Why don't you wait?'

'I've been waiting for months. Did you know that he'd deserted us? He'd just upped and left, saying he wanted to think things over. But I can't wait any longer.'

Mária's case was handled by an experienced lawyer, a friend of Granny Lizi's family, and, because it was uncontested, the divorce went through quickly. Tamás kept the car and Mária got custody of the children – so stayed in the family flat. The small plot of land near Lake Velence, bought a couple of years before, were kept in trust for Rika and Gábor.

Tamás also had to pay child maintenance. It was set by law as twenty percent after each child and was usually deducted from the man's salary by the employer and sent to the mother. Tamás said he wanted to keep the authorities out of his private life, and suggested avoiding the official route. He promised to send the money to Mária each month, personally, without the involvement of his workplace.

Mária's lawyer advised her against it. 'Why does he want to keep his divorce a secret at work? To pay less in this way?'

But Mária, wishing to put an end to all the wrangling, allowed herself to be persuaded by Tamás and agreed to his request.

Exercising his parental access rights Tamás arranged to take his children out and Mária told them that they were going to spend next Sunday with their father.

Rika and Gábor hadn't seen their father since he'd moved out. They'd been witnessing their mother's distress and daily crying, and hearing Granny Lizi vilifying him and referring to his new wife as 'that little whore'. Not being told much, they, but mostly Rika, had pieced together what was going on from snippets of adult conversation around them.

Gábor was bewildered by the situation and asked his sister: 'Is Apu not coming back? Ever again? ... But ... where is he?'

'He's not going to live with us, he lives somewhere else now', said Rika with a confidence she didn't feel. 'But he is still our daddy. And we're going to see him tomorrow'.

Although Rika provided elder sister reassurance to Gábor, she was kept awake overnight by the conflict between sympathy for their mother and guilt for her unchanged feelings towards their father. Come Sunday morning she became so agitated – should they go, do they have to go, what would they find? – that she couldn't keep her breakfast down. Mária had to give her daughter half a pill of a tranquilliser prescribed for her by a doctor friend.

Tamás took the children to the flat in Kőbánya, where his mother's council tenancy had been transferred to him. Opening the door to them was a nice, friendly lady, their father's new wife, Nadia.

Rika had not been here since Grandpa József died and hardly recognised the flat. It had been completely refurbished, with central heating, an up-to-date kitchen and a bathroom created from space in the hall. The single room was furnished in the latest style, with a sofa-bed, amoeba-shaped coffee table and sinuous armchairs on metal legs. Like a setting from an up-market interior design gallery, one of those Rika never dared go inside, only stole glimpses of through the shop windows. There were contemporary paintings and etchings on the walls, in between floor-to-ceiling shelves crammed with books, fashionably rugged ceramics and vinyl records.

Their father also looked rejuvenated, dressed in different clothes and a little slimmer than before. He seems a lot happier than he was with us, thought Rika, he's all smiles. She also saw the dissimilarities between their mother and her replacement. Nadia was a university graduate, sophisticated and modern, and, as it turned out, fifteen years younger than their father. His infatuation was obvious, he couldn't say to Nadia.

Nadia's friendly attitude towards Rika, regarding her as an intelligent grown up, was instantly disarming. She introduced Rika to some serious, highbrow music – the likes of Liszt's *Requiem*, a complete contrast to her mother's favourite operetta *The Merry Widow* – and they discovered they shared a favourite writer in Thomas Mann. To Rika this was a surprising affinity. As her mother had discouraged her children's contact with their peers, Rika had immersed herself in the world of books and her two-novels-a-week habit led to some precocious readings, leaps ahead of the light romantic novels aimed at her age-group.

Rika was pleased when Nadia noticed the signs of her early physical development and promised to go bra-shopping with her.

'We'll get something made for you,' said Nadia. 'I know where to go. I don't fit into standard sizes either. Your father always gets made-to-measure for me.'

Although embarrassed that the subject was raised in front of her father, Rika was thrilled. At home she'd been begging for a bra for ages, hoping that somehow camouflaging her growing breasts would take the wind out of her classmates' taunts. But her mother, influenced by traditional attitudes of child rearing, vetoed it as too early for a pre-teen girl, no matter how much it was actually needed.

Rika observed that Nadia's warmth and consideration had similarly won Gábor over. When he had smudges of food around his mouth, his grandmother or aunty would dab a handkerchief draped index finger with their own tongue and slick it around Gabi's mouth to wipe the stains away. He had always hated being babied like this and tried to dodge out of these attempts. Nadia, in a complete contrast, would offer *her* handkerchief to *him* to lick, an approach he seemed to find utterly charming.

After a few visits Rika suspected that Gábor had started to nurse a hope of restoring the connection he had with his father before he left them.

'I wish I could build radios with Apu again,' he whispered to her one night before going to sleep. 'Perhaps I can go and live with them. Nadia is so nice and pretty.'

Rika, not knowing how to answer, pretended to have fallen asleep.

In his new marriage Tamás's relationship with his children also changed. He suggested that they stop addressing him formally and encouraged them to talk to him and Nadia in the direct, familiar style.

One Sunday Rika wanted to borrow a book from her father and asked, 'Would Apu lend it to me?'

'You don't have to talk as if I was a third person in the

room. It's so old fashioned,' replied Tamás. 'You can simply say, can *you* lend me this book?'

The children quickly and happily switched over to this informal way of addressing their father and Granny Katus. It was much less awkward and convoluted than how they had to speak at home.

On their return home after seeing their father, Rika and Gábor were expected to give an account of the visit. Rika instinctively knew they couldn't say they had a good time, or praise anything connected to their father, let alone his new wife. Gábor also seemed to have understood, without any discussion, what his sister was trying to do and didn't mention his liking for Nadia or his fancy of going to live with them.

As they didn't want to lie to their mother, they just talked about the food they had. 'We had *gulyás* for lunch, but it was different from how *you* cook it', said Rika.

'What do you mean *you*?' Mária's reply skipped a beat, as she realised Rika used the familiar form of address. 'This is not the way to talk to your mother. Where did you learn to speak so disrespectfully?'

'Apu suggested it,' said Rika, adding 'and when we went to see Granny Katus, she didn't mind it, she liked it.'

'And it's so much easier,' chipped in Gábor.

'I don't care if it's easier, you are not to use it, not with me', insisted Mária.

But as the children's talk frequently slipped into the familiar form after this and she got tired of correcting them, Mária gradually accepted this mode of address, though still hadn't given up other aspects of her traditional parenting.

Shortly after his marriage to Nadia, Tamás's workplace was making plans to send him on an official posting to Cuba, to develop its electronic industry, in the internationalist spirit of one Socialist country helping another.

On an impulse, Tamás mentioned the possibility of taking Gábor with them. 'We may be able to arrange it ... a boy could go and live with the father after a divorce. Would you like to come with us?' he asked his son casually. Although he knew that it all depended on the consent of his ex-wife, who had custody of the children and may not agree, he dangled the prospect in front of his son, without thinking it through.

Gábor, almost ten now, took his father's vague suggestion as cast iron certainty and was overjoyed that his hopes were going to become reality.

But the children had heard no more on the subject until some weeks later the visit to their father turned out to be one of goodbye. Gábor was crushingly disappointed. 'But Apu, you said you'd take me with you,' he said in tears.

Tamás, who had long forgotten his own hasty promise and hadn't actually done anything towards making it happen, said to his son, 'Your mother wouldn't agree to it and there was nothing I could do to change her mind.'

Tamás flew off to Havana days later and disappeared from his children's life again. He was no letter writer and what scant news Rika and Gábor had of him were conveyed to them by his brother.

A few months after Tamás's departure Uncle Pál invited his niece and nephew. After his own marriage had broken down and his wife left taking their young daughter with her, he now lived in the flat on Gellért Hill with his mother. He told Mária on the phone that he wanted Rika and Gábor to visit their grandmother.

When they arrived at Uncle Pál's flat it was their grandmother who opened the door. Although she looked frail, Granny Katus appeared to be no less active than before. She welcomed her grandchildren with home-made *málnaszörp* and showed them the big glass containers, full of raspberries layered with sugar, brewing in the sunshine on the south facing balcony. When the foam on the top cleared, Granny explained, she would sieve it, pour it into bottles and then sterilize it for next year's supply of the cordial.

Uncle Pál came home from work a little later and revealed the real purpose of his invitation. He wanted to tape messages from the children onto cassettes to send to their father.

The recording equipment was set up on the desk in Uncle Pál's study, where he also slept. While Gábor spotted that the reel-to-reel tape recorder was the same model his father used, Rika checked out the towers of books by the bed. All serious looking volumes on science, history or philosophy, many in foreign languages. She recognised only one name, Bertrand Russell's, among the writers.

When it came to talking into the microphone Rika and Gábor were tongue-tied. They did not know what to say to their father following the latest, now months-long break in their connection. Uncle Pál tried to draw them out by asking about school, about their readings, what they liked and disliked or things they had done, and they finally got going.

After the children had finished their own recordings, Rika caught Uncle's summary to his brother – he thought she didn't hear him in the other room – about their unsophisticated tastes influenced by their mother's non-intellectual preferences. It was like a bucket of cold water on her head and she thought it most unfair.

The tapes were sent off to Cuba, Rika and Gábor assumed, but they received no replies.

They missed their father, whose absence from their life had now become complete. Rika thought they just had to get on with the situation they found themselves in, since they were powerless to change it. She buried herself in books.

Gábor became noticeably withdrawn. He didn't say much, even to Rika, but she understood that he believed his father was lost to him forever. With the wisdom of her two-and-a-half-years of seniority she tried to raise his spirits: 'These years will be over quickly and he'll be back. And when you're fourteen, you may be able to go and live with him.'

8

Single Parenting

The collapse of her marriage cracked the foundations of Mária's world. In the mid-1960s divorce was still so unusual in Hungary that in her daughter's class at school there was only one other girl out of forty whose parents were not together. The Roman Catholic Church did not recognise it, and people generally disapproved of it and regarded it as suspicious or shameful.

She had always done what was required of her, always fulfilled her duties as a wife and mother, she thought, she didn't deserve to be abandoned. It was important to her that what people saw of her life reflected well on her – a nicely kept, spotless flat, a husband who provided for the family as he should, and well behaved and looked after children, who were successful at school. Being deserted by her husband was a shattering blow to her carefully maintained public image.

Her self-confidence as a woman was also badly dented; she couldn't understand why she was rejected. How could it happen to her – to the popular and pretty teenager, to the much courted young woman, to the mother of two beautiful children? She had looked after herself and not let herself go. Even after two pregnancies she still had not grown fat, she'd kept her figure. So why had things turned out like this, why was she discarded? She could only find the answer in Tamás's fickleness, in the unreliability and treacherousness of men in general and in her bad luck in life.

Having become a single parent, Mária had to go out and get a job, as the only income they had was child support from Tamás, not enough for the three of them to live on. Through the connection of a family friend she found a position as a lab assistant at a veterinary research institute that was developing animal vaccines against common infections, such as foot and mouth disease. She had no relevant experience, but the work was not difficult to learn, involving lots of repetitive manual processes for the preparation and testing of materials. And while her monthly salary was modest, there were a few perks to the job. At the conclusion of a series of experiments the lab workers were allowed take away the untreated control animals, chickens or rabbits, which found their way into stews and roasts at home. Since the use of pure alcohol in the lab was not monitored, 'liberated' litres of it were transformed into home-made chocolate liqueur or egg-flip before Christmas or Easter.

It felt daunting to Mária to leave the protection of her home and start her first proper, official job in her mid-thirties, but earning her own money meant she was no longer dependent on anybody. This liberating realisation filtered through into the advice she gave to her daughter, 'Study and get a profession, so that you'd never have to rely on a man!'

Even so, after the divorce had come through she didn't go back to her maiden name but continued as Mrs Tamás Varga, as if nothing had changed, despite nothing being the same any more.

After Mária had gone out to work – the visibility of a working woman replacing the hiddenness of a housewife – there were several men, colleagues and acquaintances, who wanted to hook up with the attractive divorcee. She resisted all these attempts, turning down even innocent invitations to coffee, with a repeated and stereotypical objection, 'Men think a divorcée is fair game to prey on.' The caution induced by her painful experience with Tamás resulted in a generalised distrust of men.

The only man who breached her defences was Géza, her lawyer throughout the divorce proceedings. Perhaps it was because he was a family friend and she had come to trust him. Perhaps because he was fifteen years older than her and unlikely to cheat on her. Perhaps because his wife was in a sanatorium with a chronic illness, and marriage – or the threat of that trap in Mária's eyes – was not immediately on the cards.

Géza had a grand first floor apartment overlooking Oktogon Square on People's Republic Avenue – the current name of the once elegant, pre-war Andrássy Avenue, following its renaming as Stalin Street in 1950 and briefly as Avenue of Hungarian Youth during the 1956 uprising. He was the head of a lawyers' cooperative, where he spent most of his days and evenings. He lived like a bachelor, taking his meals in the restaurant at the foot of his building and was looked after by a housekeeper who came several times a week. His parqueted living room with the three large windows facing the square was sparsely furnished – just a couple of stuffed-to-overflowing bookshelves and a huge writing desk piled high with legal documents folded lengthwise and tied up with black cloth ribbons, plus a pair of armchairs in a corner seating area. The lack of curtains or carpets echoed under footsteps. The impression given was that this was his private lawyer's office, rather than his home. There was a conspicuous absence of any evidence of a woman's touch.

Mária and Géza saw each other frequently: he took her out to dinner, to the Opera or on a trip to Vienna; later on she stayed overnight in his apartment or went away at weekends with him and his friends. But they lived apart, conducting separate lives. He was very keen on her and would have liked to marry her, when he became free. She enjoyed being wooed and appreciated, which went some way towards restoring her self-confidence. But she said repeatedly that she did not want to give Rika and Gábor a step-father.

After Tamás vanished from the family scene, Mária focused most of her attention on coping with the practical problems of their changed situation. In the morning she had to leave for work before the children walked to school, so Rika was entrusted with a key to the flat and charged with getting herself and Gábor there and back. In the afternoon Mária came home a couple hours after her children, and had to organise everything for the next day, shop for the daily groceries and cook lunch, to be re-heated on returning from school by Rika. Granny Lizi came to look after the children one day a week, but Aunty

Hilda's help they could no longer afford. Although Rika was required to do more of the chores as she got older, housework still claimed many of Mária's Saturday afternoons before she could get some rest on Sunday.

Beyond the logistics of being a single mother, on top of recovering from her own hurt and re-building her self-esteem, Mária hadn't got much mental energy left for paying attention to how their father's disappearance affected her children.

Rika seemed all right, not too affected by the divorce, Mária reckoned, there was no need to worry about her. She was studious and most marks in her semester school reports had been excellent. She would almost certainly get through the entrance exam for the *gimnázium*. As she should, with her head always in a book. And a good daughter, relieving some of the burden of housework from her mother's shoulder. Even if she was growing a little disobedient lately.

Gábor was different. He had been at the top of his class in his first couple of years at school, but his results had started going downhill after his father had moved out. Then, following Tamás's departure for Cuba, he'd become noticeably and increasingly downcast, withdrawn and silent, or occasionally swinging into insolent reactions against his mother.

'Why do I have to go to bed now? Apu would have let me stay up late.'

'I hate doing homework. I hate school. I wish I could've gone with them to Cuba!'

'You never allow me to do anything I want! If only I could live with him ...'

Mária felt her son was holding her responsible for

something. But for what and why? Wasn't she the injured party in the divorce, and therefore due special consideration? Wasn't she doing her best in this difficult situation? Was she to blame that Tamás abandoned his children? Anyway, what does a boy of Gábor's age understand?

As Mária was now a working woman, with only a two-week annual leave, Rika and Gábor spent more of the summers at their mother's parents. One year on arriving at Albertfalva they announced: 'We're not going to church any more, because we don't believe in God'.

Granny Lizi was shocked. She was aware that her grandchildren's declaration was made in the atmosphere of the Communist regime's underlying philosophy of atheism. But she thought – she had hoped – that family influence would override indoctrination at school. What especially hurt her was that the driving force of this rebellion was her favourite, Gábor, not yet eleven, whose all-round spirit of defiance was mirroring the intellectual attitude of his father and his other grandmother.

'But how can you live without faith?' asked Granny Lizi in desperation.

'Easily', replied Rika cheekily, before she and Gábor pointed out how their mother was managing quite well, despite almost never going to church.

It was not only with regards to religion that Granny Lizi sought to influence her grandchildren's upbringing. Going by the example of her own girlhood, which she had replayed with her own daughters, Lizi applied the same approach with her granddaughter. Rika had to be sheltered from the facts of life, to keep her 'innocent' as long as possible and to protect her from all possible corrupting influences. Even after Rika had gone trough puberty Lizi tried to shield her from knowledge of anything considered unsuitable, on one occasion stepping in front of the TV to block her granddaughter's view, to prevent her from seeing scenes of a woman giving birth.

Following her divorce Mária carried on in the traditional style of parenting, which was what she had been used to and she saw no reason to change it. It was a world where the parents laid down the law and the children had to obey. But now all authority was concentrated in her sole person. As her children were morphing into rebellious adolescents, they resented being told what to do or what not to do, and became increasingly defiant. Mária found it difficult to control them or to relate to them in any other way.

Rika and Gábor's frequently voiced complaint was that their mother treated them as children and did not involve them in the making of family decisions. Mária's attitude was that she was the one in charge, so did not feel the need to discuss with her children – what's more, deliberately concealed – the sale of the small plot of land that was left in trust for them in the divorce settlement.

Mária had, in fact, no choice but to sell. They needed extra money for larger, one-off purchases – a washing machine or a TV, when they broke down – and there were no available funds to build on the plot, which the original sale agreement obliged them to. If she had talked it over with Rika and Gábor, if she had described the financial straits they were in, they would certainly have seen that selling the plot was unavoidable. But they'd only found out about it when it was already a done deal, by accident, from an unguarded remark of Granny Lizi's. They thought their mother's behaviour was unforgivable.

In clashes with her children Mária always had the last words and a trump card up her sleeve. 'While you live under my roof, while you eat my bread, you have to obey me. If you don't like it here, you can go to your father's. Then, when you're fourteen, you can choose which parent you want to live with. Until then, you have to do as you're told.'

She meant it as an ultimatum and a threat, not realising that for her children it slowly turned into a desirable escape route. But it didn't apply to Rika – according to the law, only boys could decide if they wanted to go and to live with their father after a divorce.

At the age of fourteen Rika finished primary school and got a place at a *gimnázium,* one of the top five in Budapest. It was nearby, just five minutes walk away from her old school.

The form teacher asked to see the parents of the new intake of students before the first semester. Mr Béres duly registered that in Rika's case the official caregiver was not the father, but the single-parent mother. He also enquired if Mária minded her occupation of laboratory assistant being recorded as 'working class'.

'It would look better in our statistics, if we could show to the Ministry a greater proportion of pupils of working class origin.'

Mária didn't need convincing. But Mr Béres continued, 'And changing her background category from 'intellectual class', according to her father's occupation, should help her later, if she wants to go to university.'

'It doesn't make any difference to me, just go ahead,' said Mária, thinking Mr Béres was banging on open doors.

Once Rika had started at the *gimnázium* she was considered old enough to get a month-long paid job during the school holidays to help with the family finances. 'From what you'll earn we can buy new winter boots for you,' said Mária.

The first of these vacation jobs was at the Ikarus bus factory, where the father of one of Rika's classmates worked. Every morning at 5am the special mini-bus picked her and other workers up in front of the Eastern Railway Station and took them to the factory site on the edge of Budapest.

Rika's task at the factory was to insert a plastic covering into the middle groove of a metal strip hiding the joint between two side-panels on the buses being manufactured. Not hard on its own, but the frequency required and the speed of the assembly line proved an unrelenting time-tyranny. During the third week she was almost swept into the two metre-deep, concrete construction pit by the inexorably moving line and a veteran colleague yanked her away from disaster at the very last second. Deeply shaken by this, Rika packed the job in before her monthly contract was completed, not even waiting for the promised bonus.

The summer jobs she took on in the following years were less arduous: working in an ice-cream kiosk or in a patisserie or as a clothes-check attendant at a swimming pool. Though they didn't pay as well as the factory did, as long as her wages covered the cost of the next necessary purchase, it was enough.

To find goods in the shops you actually wanted to buy was another matter.

After Rika had outgrown the last sheepskin coat bought for her before her parent's divorce, she needed something new for the cold winters. Looking in the regular clothing shops she and her mother couldn't find anything affordable that she liked. Then Rika had heard about a warehouse-like place that sold surplus clothing for people working in outdoor occupations. She went there on her own and bought a dark, heavy, double-breasted item, made for a man. Her mother disapproved, but couldn't do much about it, as her daughter had earned the money for it and the deal was done. So for a few years Rika wore in proud rebellion what was always referred to as her 'postman's coat'.

Next year she wanted a handbag and had in mind a plain, satchel-like shape, with a flap and a shoulder strap, nothing fancy. After an afternoon search in all the department stores, she returned home with her purchase, but in tears. What she had bought, she hated already. Made from some dull, plasticky material, not even pretend-leather, it was just awful looking and unpleasant to the touch. It really upset her having had to spend her summer earnings on something so repulsive, because there was nothing else. And every time she used the hideous thing she would be reminded of what a waste of money it was.

At the *gimnázium* Rika became part of a group of classmates, boys and girls, who hung out together or went to gigs or the cinema at the weekends. Sándor, a gentle, thoughtful boy, one of the cleverest in the class, became her boyfriend. He wrote romantic poems for her after walking hand-in-hand in the snow-covered City Park. *Beautiful was the snow crunching under our feet / and beautiful the feelings we discovered in our hearts.* Rika was flattered and touched by the sentiments, but secretly thought he was better at maths than at poetry.

When Mária had found out that Rika had a boyfriend, she hit the roof and declared, 'You will not go out with a boy on a date until you are eighteen.'

Although later she eased up on the absolute prohibition, she continued to exercise control over when and how Rika could go out, only allowing her to meet Sándor for an hour on a Saturday afternoon, or sending Gábor to sit with them at a cinema matinee on a Sunday. She also forbade her daughter to invite anybody – meaning Sándor – to the flat after school and before she arrived home from work.

The consequence of all these vetoes was that Rika resorted to lies, pretending to be at a fictitious poetry rehearsal or studying at a girlfriend's place after school, when in fact she was at Sándor's home – his parents didn't mind what *he* was up to – engaged in the tentative discovery of each other's bodies. 'Doesn't my mother realise that her suspicions of what we might be up to are in effect *giving* us ideas?' she said to him.

Rika was well aware that the reason behind all the prohibitions was her mother's unspoken fear of her daughter becoming pregnant while still at school. But she thought talking about it would have been more effective in preventing that dreaded outcome.

Mother-daughter talks, however, were not part of Mária's

parenting repertoire. When Rika got her first period it caught her completely unprepared. Neither her mother nor her grandmother enlightened her before puberty about her soon to be changing biology. Coming home from school in tears, with unexpected bleeding, she was simply given a few rags by Granny Lizi and was briefly told how to deal with the practicalities of the monthly curse.

There were no lessons on sex and related matters at school either. In the end through a friend's enlightened parent Rika had got hold of a popular science book on love and relationships and sex and contraception. The book took up residence under her knickers in the chest of drawers and was taken out for surreptitious readings in her mother's absence. Until the day when her mother came home early and caught her in the act – of reading, not sex – and confiscated the book.

What Rika had learnt from that book led to a bizarre conversation a few months later. Granny Lizi was staying with them for the day and Rika asked her grandmother for a shoe cream for cleaning her white plimsolls. After rummaging around in a few places in her daughter's flat Lizi handed her granddaughter a small tube.

Rika burst out laughing. 'But Grandma, this is not shoe cream, this is the contraceptive jelly mother keeps in the pocket of her bathrobe, next to her Dutch cap.'

Without comment or asking her granddaughter how she knew all this, Lizi put the tube back where she'd found it, and gave Rika some money to get shoe cream from the corner shop.

Through her workplace Mária was able to have access to the

same holiday complex by the Balaton they had gone to as a family before Tamás had left. She would spend her regular two weeks' vacations there with Rika and Gábor, then she had to go back to work and her mother came down from Budapest and took over.

For the next week or two Granny Lizi was in charge of her grandchildren. They rented a room in a private house with bunk beds and straw mattresses for the three of them. There was no bathroom, only a pit-toilet with a wooden seat and cut-up newspaper squares on a string. They fetched water from a neighbour's well for washing and bathed in the lake. Lunch was usually a pre-paid set-meal at a small eating house, or *süllő* from the fried food kiosk, because you had to try a pike-perch from Lake Balaton if you stayed near there. Rika and Gábor liked the strangeness of their quasi-camping experiences and enjoyed the absence of the restrictions imposed on them at home.

The summer when Rika turned fifteen Lizi had truly come into her duties as a chaperone. One night a few older boys Rika had met at the lake-side beach knocked on their window after they'd gone to bed. Granny Lizi scrambled out of her lower bunk-bed and in her long nightgown, her hair in curlers, confronted the boys with guard-dog fierceness.

'Go away! How dare you come to pester us. She's not that kind of girl. Go away, or I'll call the police.'

She'd doubled her vigilance after this, keeping an eye on anybody who got near her granddaughter. Not that any of those boys had the courage to provoke her fury again.

Although the health of Mária's father had been a source of

constant worry to the family over the years, it was Granny Lizi who died first. She was in her mid-sixties. One autumn evening she complained about feeling unwell but Grandpa László didn't call an ambulance until the next morning. By the time she was taken to hospital it was too late, it turned out she'd suffered a heart attack and could not be saved.

In addition to his grief over losing his wife of over forty years, László felt utterly helpless. Like most men of his generation, he'd left the organisation of their domestic life to his wife and now that she was suddenly gone, he was unable to cope. His daughters had to step in. The daily lunch menu was ordered for him at the small neighbourhood restaurant and Mária's sister, Blondie, who didn't have a job, took care of the household tasks. Mária had her father stay with her at Thököly Road for one or two nights a week, an arrangement that lasted till the end of his life.

The year after Granny Lizi's death Blondie's son Laci turned eighteen and moved in with his grandfather. Laci actually needed somewhere to live as he had been kicked out from home by his father. Tibor was an authoritarian figure who regularly belted his son into obedience. As Laci had become an adolescent, the clashes between them intensified, because Tibor could not tolerate the independent will of his son. Having been conditioned from an early age, Laci dared not raise a hand against his father, not even in defence. His suppressed feelings only found outlets in recurring nightmares, in which he attacked his father with a cut-throat razor. The beatings continued, even after Laci had grown into a tall, powerfully built young man. Then one day something snapped in him: seeing another assault coming, he put out his hand to stop his father, then, towering over him, grabbed hold of both of his father's wrists. Tibor, spluttering in incoherent rage but immobilised and powerless, ordered his son out of his flat and his life.

Having lost the emotional support of her mother, Mária got friendly with one of her neighbours, a woman of a decade her senior.

Rózsi supplemented her widow's pension by renting out a couple of rooms in her flat through IBUSZ, the official state tourist agency. Some of her guests came for short stays: construction workers on the first nuclear power plant or bauxite miners up in the capital on a few days' leave – the 'aristocracy' in the workers' democracy, with the spending power to match. Her steady income, however, was secured by providing long term lodgings to men from country towns and villages, who worked in the factories of Budapest. The employers of these men simply rented rooms for their workers in the home of private individuals, instead of putting them up in workers' hostels.

Rózsi filled a companion space in Mária's daily life and soon became her confidant. Mária spent increasing lengths of time after work with Rózsi, having coffee or drinks in her kitchen, and chatting to her lodgers, who tried to chat her up.

Frequently when Uncle Géza called it was Rika who answered the phone in her mother's absence, and had to go over to Aunty Rózsi's and get her mother to the phone. Rika was also instructed not to reveal to Uncle Géza where her mother had been or for how long, and she found the fibs that were required more and more tricky and uncomfortable to pull off.

Rózsi always said what Mária wanted to hear.

She backed her when Mária complained about her children's misbehaviour. 'They don't appreciate the sacrifices that you've made for them. You could've got married again and gave them a stepfather.'

When Mária lamented Géza's less-than-complete devotion to her, Rózsi egged her on. 'He's stringing you along, honey. He'll never be free to marry you. And he's too old for you.'

She also encouraged Mária not to ignore the advances of her guests and lodgers, 'Go ahead, honey, you deserve a bit of happiness! After all that you've gone through!'

9

After Cuba

'Have you had Coca-Cola before?' asked Tamás.

In the summer of 1968, back from his Cuban assignment after three years away, he invited his children to the speciality *cukrászda* on People's Republic Avenue. The luxury patisserie was almost empty on this weekday afternoon, as the prices here were much higher than elsewhere. When the white-capped, frilly-aproned waitress brought their order to the marble-topped table – double espresso for him, Dobos torte with a shroud of whipped cream for Gábor and ice cream for Rika – it was accompanied by curvy bottles of a brown fizzy drink.

He was fairly certain that the answer would be 'No', as the previously dubbed 'symbol of Western imperialism' was just beginning to be produced in Budapest and was only available in a few exclusive places.

'I have come across it on our journey back from Cuba', said Tamás proudly, as if he had personally been involved in bringing it to Hungary. 'I liked it straight away and wanted you to taste it.'

He was trying to impress them and to make amends.

He had been back for months. His suntan was beginning to fade. He knew he should have called them before. But he couldn't take his children to the flat in Kőbánya, to that scene of constant battles with Nadia. He couldn't be sure how she would react to them now.

His children had changed a lot in the time he'd been away. Rika was almost sixteen now, petite and slightly plump, and Gábor, a lanky thirteen-year-old, already taller than his sister. Silently they sipped their drinks through straws and looked at their father warily, as though at a stranger.

He regaled them with tales of his adventures. 'I shook hands with Fidel Castro. Imagine that! After we'd arrived the whole Hungarian trade delegation were taken to the Palace of the Revolution and introduced to him.' He didn't mention having had to listen afterwards to a three-hour-long speech of *El Comandante* on economic cooperation between Communist countries.

'And I met Che Guevara, ... on his last public appearance in Havana, as it turned out. He was the Minister of Industries at the time. He was never seen after that.'

He also told them he had fallen in love with the Cuban way of life. 'The people are so friendly and the climate is wonderful, it makes you so relaxed. Of course I've learnt Spanish, the Latin I did at school made it very easy, I'm quite fluent now', he boasted. He was keen to prove his proficiency as dancer, by getting up from the table and demonstrating his salsa moves in the near empty *cukrászda,* humming his favourite number, *Bésame mucho.*

Although the alcove they were sitting in was half hidden by

the framing velvet drapes, Rika could hear the sniggering of the waitresses in the background. She remembered the saying 'He who comes from afar, can spin tall tales' and wondered if this whole performance was their father's strategy to avoid having to explain why he hadn't been in contact with them these past years.

'But where is Nadia? Why is she not here?' asked Gábor the obvious questions, remembering the pretty and kind would-be step-mother, who flitted in and out of their lives a few years ago.

'You know, Nadia didn't like living in Havana. Well, she did at first. But then I was away at work all day, and she was cooped up in this flat they'd given us in a high-rise block. Sometimes the water was cut off, sometimes the electricity was switched off for hours, and finding food was a struggle .... You know, they have food rationing there, the *libreta* system of subsidised basic items, but if you wanted more or something better, you had to search for it and pay extra on the free market. I had a good salary by local standards, so we could afford it, that wasn't the problem. But the constant daily battles wore her down. She felt she was reduced to the status of a housewife, of a dependent, she, a university graduate, an independent-minded woman.'

Hearing their father's long confession, so uncharacteristic of him, Rika and Gábor dared not interrupt him.

Tamás continued, 'Then, I thought having children would make things better. But when Nadia suspected she might be pregnant, she threatened to throw herself off the roof. She was too highly strung. She was neurotic, to tell the truth.'

'And what happened then?' Rika cut in, stunned by the revelation.

'From then on, things went from bad to worse. We quarrelled and fought every day. Since we've come back to Budapest, I've had to go to work with evidence of the previous night's battle on my face. Courtesy of her long, manicured nails. One set of bloody scratches just getting healed before being replaced by another. And all our nice ceramics reduced to shards in these skirmishes.'

'So, you see why I couldn't take you to the flat in Kőbánya. But, she'll move out soon, the divorce is already under way.'

Despite the failure of his second marriage, things weren't looking altogether too bad for Tamás. After a long official stationing abroad he was allowed to bring back, without paying import tax, covetable Western goods, unobtainable in Socialist Hungary. His new car, a Ford Taunus, became a status symbol in a country where people had to register to be on a waiting list of several years before they could buy a Trabant, a Škoda or a Polski Fiat, cars produced in a COMECON country, which did not need scarce hard currency to import.

He had offered to the council his mother's old flat, which he had refurbished, and in exchange got a modern two-room one with a balcony, a kitchen-diner and a proper bathroom in a high rise, purpose built block. The next time he met up with his children he took them to this new place of his. Rika recognised the furniture from the previous flat. 'Nadia did not want to take anything when she left', said Tamás.

His return from Cuba coincided with the beginning of the New Economic Mechanism – reforms that aimed to introduce certain market elements into the centrally planned economy of

Hungary. It gave state firms and enterprises a degree of independence in decision making and allowed them to reward individual talent and contribution. As Tamás's professional standing was hugely boosted by the Cuban posting he was soon promoted to be the head of his department in the Industrial Research Institute for Telecommunications.

Looking out of his first-floor office Tamás noticed a slender young woman – hardly more than a girl – surrounded by a gaggle of young men in the courtyard of the Research Institute. The scene was repeated almost daily, with the same girl smoking and joking with a constantly changing combination of admirers. From his vantage point it looked like bees buzzing around a honey pot.

Uncle Jon – the workplace elder a couple of years short of retirement and a reliable source of information – was ready to supply the background details.

'Éva's been helping out in the general office for a few months. Apparently, she's left secondary school without taking the *érettségi* exam, but got a job here because her father knew somebody in Personnel.'

'Do you know if she has a boyfriend?' Tamás came straight to the point.

'I don't know,' said Uncle Jon. 'I gather she still lives with her parents, but she's very popular and has been seen leaving work with different lads.'

In the next few weeks Tamás got into conversations with Éva at the lunchtime canteen. She was lively and flirtatious and had a pretty face and a lithe body, barely concealed by her clothes. She had all the allure of her eighteen years. No wonder, he thought, the boys couldn't leave her alone.

She told him that she had been always been sporty, a gymnast in fact, and because she was slim, she was recruited into modelling clothes for fashion shows at the clothing factory where her father worked. It was easy money, practically effortless, and the success of this made her regard studying as pointless. She was an only child and her working-class parents, not highly educated, she confessed, did not push her to continue with her education, and that's why she had not finished school.

Tamás, twenty-three years her senior, eventually got up his courage to ask Éva out to dinner and she, flattered by the attention of the boss, accepted.

He took her to the famous Gundel restaurant in City Park in his Ford Taunus. Éva looked uncomfortable in this unaccustomed setting and stood out in her mini dress among the staid middle-aged clientèle, but Tamás felt proud of his nubile young date. Entertaining her he pulled out all the stops, even asking the resident Gypsy band, to her obvious embarrassment, to play something for her.

After the restaurant's closing time at eleven he drove Éva home to the working-class district of Újpest. Her parents were waiting up for their daughter and invited him in. They took to him straight away, especially when he declined her father's offer of a shot of *pálinka*, pointing out that he was driving.

This put the seal of her parents' approval on their relationship.

'He looks like a dependable, responsible man,' said Éva's father to his wife as they were settling into bed. He wanted to believe that, despite having not much evidence for it. 'And prosperous enough. Our Évike will have a secure future with him.'

Following the tacit acceptance by Éva's parents, Tamás intensified his charm offensive by plying her with presents, and wining and dining her regularly. As they got to know each other better, she came to appreciate his gifts and the lifestyle he could offer her. Within a few short months he asked her to move in with him, to his new flat, and pressed her to quit her job at the Institute. 'It wouldn't look good if they'd discovered that we live together. Anyway, you don't need that job any more, I'll support you.'

On their next visit to see their father Rika and Gábor found Éva firmly ensconced in their father's flat. At first the situation struck Rika as bizarre – meeting a prospective step-mother a couple of years older than herself – but both she and her brother got on well with Éva, who was practically their own generation and fairly easy to relate to.

It took no time at all for Éva to come to regard Rika as a girlfriend and to start bragging to her about all the things Tamás bought for her.

'Let me show you this safari suit your father's got me. The jacket will have to be altered to be more tight-fitting and the skirt will have to be shortened, but it's the latest style.'

Rika had to admit that the suit looked very good on Éva's slim figure. She looked just like one of the fashion plates from the magazine *Burda*, which lay open on the kitchen counter and which was only available from a Váci Street newsagent aimed at foreign tourists. Rika envied the figure of the model, but not the outfit, which wouldn't have suited her own curvier, shorter body anyway.

She looked at the label. It was from the Luxus Department Store, the exclusive place where you could buy Western fashion. The price, correspondingly luxury too, made her gasp. She didn't have a lot of clothes and most of them were made at home by her mother. You couldn't usually find clothes you wanted to buy in ordinary shops, or if you very rarely did, as it was starting to happen recently, they were too expensive.

Éva continued to prattle on, sashaying in front of the mirror. 'It's just the thing I need for a seaside holiday. Your father's promised to take me to Lloret de Mar next summer.'

'Isn't suede too thick a material for summer? It's quite hot in Spain,' Rika voiced some common sense.

'Oh, I don't mind about that. I just want to wear clothes that are in fashion. And not what everybody else's wearing.'

Did she realise, thought Rika, that very few people in the country could afford such clothes, or, for that matter, a Spanish holiday? Were she and Tamás aware that his children had to live much more frugally than they did? Was she insensitive? Or unthinking?

But all she said aloud, 'That's wonderful. It should be a great holiday for you.'

While Rika and Éva had girly chats in the bedroom, Gábor was watching the weekend football matches in the living room with Tamás.

Gábor had warmed up to his father slowly, cautiously after

his return to Budapest. He had unspoken questions, he felt things needed addressing. Why wasn't he taken to Cuba as had been promised? That sudden, seemingly last minute reversal, what was the reason? During those years abroad, why had his father never written to him? None of this was explained or even mentioned. He knew that if he'd brought any of this up, he would only get a clever wisecrack or a glib non-answer. The relationship between his childhood self and his father could never be re-captured. You could never step into the same river twice. He felt they had to start from the current situation. Now he was fourteen, there was no more building radios together. His father's attention was focused on his current and future family. The only link Gábor could have with him was enjoying football and cheering their team Fradi on together.

Éva confided to Rika the misery of her repeated miscarriages. 'I don't know what's wrong, why I'm losing these pregnancies, after a month or two. It's most upsetting. It must be my fault. And your father is very keen for us to have children.'

In the end, sparing no expense, Tamás took Éva to a private gynaecologist. After extensive tests it was discovered that Éva's body was not producing an enzyme that was necessary to sustain a pregnancy. The doctor suggested a course of medication to make up for the deficiency and Éva reported to Rika that she and Tamás had hopefully and enthusiastically embarked on their baby-making project.

'You know, I like sex with your father,' said Éva. 'It's so much better with him than with my previous boyfriends. They all finished far too quickly. I enjoy that it lasts longer with him. I even like his weight pressing down on me.'

Rika was taken a little aback by the sharing of such intimate confidences about her father, but thought it would be too prudish to object. She told herself that Éva was simply very open about such matters, truly liberated when it came to sex, and didn't have conventional hang-ups. Éva was obviously at ease with her body, had nothing to be ashamed of, and was so uninhibited, it didn't occur to her that not everybody was like that. On hot summer days she walked around in the flat in a micro-bikini, seemingly unaware of the effect it had on Gábor.

It was such a contrast with Rika's own uptight upbringing. She was still a virgin and had not given in to the gentle pressure from her boyfriend. But she was planning to go on holiday with Sándor after they'd finished school and would certainly make use of Éva's promised help to get the contraceptive pill prescribed before her eighteenth birthday.

Rika's fledgling romance with Sándor, however, didn't make it that far.

In the second half of their last year at the *gimnázium* they didn't see much of each other at school as the graduating students were allowed to prepare for the *érettségi* at home. She noticed that he no longer phoned to ask her out. Although she knew that they had to study hard, as their future depended on the result of these exams, she couldn't believe that that was the true explanation for his silence. She suspected that he got fed up with having their dates rationed by her mother or cancelled as punishment for something she had done.

But she was too proud to find out what the real reason

might be. She reckoned that if *she* had called him herself she would risk a more-than-likely rebuff. So without acknowledgement on either side their relationship withered to death.

To avoid an embarrassing meeting with him, and perhaps being humiliated in front of her classmates, she ducked out of going to the school prom and did not even take part in the photo session for the graduation tableau for their class of 1970. After the summer holiday their paths would diverge for good – she would begin university straight away in the autumn and he would have to do a year of military service before starting his course. She would never need to meet him again.

With Éva as the catalyst, Rika and Gábor's relationship with their father became a little closer. They saw him frequently, no longer as part of the stipulated parental access visits, which their father had effectively given up, but on their own initiatives, calling him at his workplace and turning up at his flat.

Their growing dissatisfaction with the situation at home found receptive ears in their father. They told him about the arguments with their mother, of her authoritarian attitude and their constant battles with her for just a little independence. Tamás responded by egging them on and offering alternative interpretations and different spins on past events.

He said to Rika, 'No, you were definitely *not* a premature baby. That's simply what your mother wanted everybody to believe. She made that up when you were born not a full nine months after our wedding. She didn't want people to suspect that she wasn't a virgin on her wedding day.'

With a casual aside he was stoking Gábor's resentment. 'Your mother didn't really want to have you, she wanted to have an abortion when she got pregnant with you. She pretended it was for medical reasons, but that wasn't true.'

He told them that he wanted to *disszidál* after the crushing of the 1956 uprising, and that he was thwarted in his intentions because 'your mother didn't want to be parted from her mother'.

He also hinted that his first marriage broke down not because of *his* extra-marital affair and suggested that the blame lay with Mária, that *she* had a lover.

Some of his remarks were channelled through Éva, who breezily told Rika: 'According to your father, Mária was more interested in housework or the weekly laundry than sex with her husband.'

Rika and Gábor felt very uncomfortable hearing these comments and insinuations, and understood perfectly the motivation behind them. They thought maybe it was not so wise after all to confide in their father and to try to find an ally in him against their mother. They felt like pawns in the long term, still ongoing blame game of their parents.

But the times right after their parents' divorce, when they tried not to take sides in the conflict, had been long gone. Now it was a question of balancing the two sides. Besides, their father's 'revelations' fitted quite believably into how they now regarded their mother and they needed somebody on their side in their battles with her. So they continued to keep in touch with their father and friendly with Éva.

Immediately after his second divorce was finalised, Tamás

proposed to Éva, wanting to put their de facto relationship on an official footing. He told his children of their plan and invited them to the wedding, which was to take place in a couple of months' time in late spring.

It was Rika's last year at school and cramming for the *érettségi* meant not having to attend regular classes, so she had time on her hands to help with the wedding preparations, even accompanying the bride-to-be on a shopping trip for her wedding dress.

At the bridal boutique on elegant Váci Street Éva emerged from the changing cubicle into the glittering, mirrored front area of the salon, in outfit after modest outfit. Rika was surprised by Éva's choices, so unlike her usual figure-revealing style.

After Éva selected her preferred model, which had to be adjusted to her figure, she called Rika into the be-curtained cubicle. There, standing in her underwear, she revealed the reason behind her choices. 'I've just found out that I'm pregnant. Your father's over the moon, but this wedding dress will have to be big enough for my expanding stomach.'

Unfortunately, a few days later Éva miscarried again; the gynaecologist's latest treatment solution hadn't worked. She and Tamás were upset, but they consoled themselves that she was young and they could continue trying. And she took this opportunity to change the roomy wedding gown she'd settled on for the white mini dress she'd originally wanted.

On the big day Rika and Gábor arrived at their father's flat in the morning, finding Éva's parents already there. Rika helped with the bride's hairdo by back-combing and lacquering it into a flower-decorated beehive and Éva did her own make up with heavy mascara, a flicked upper eye line and pale pink lips.

Then it was time to set out for the registry office, but the flowers they ordered had still not been delivered to the flat. So with the rest of the party leaving in Tamás's car, Rika took a taxi to the florist on the other side of town to collect the bridal bouquet and the buttonholes, and took them directly to the wedding venue, getting there with just a few minutes to spare.

The ceremony was attended by Éva's parents and Tamás's children, and a couple of his colleagues as witnesses. Neither his mother, Katus, nor his brother, Pál was present.

Afterwards they celebrated with a small informal dinner in the garden of a traditional restaurant. Uncle Jon, in his best man's speech, expressed a hope that Tamás had finally found his ideal life partner. 'I hope it will be third time lucky for you!' He toasted their happiness with his favourite beer, Radeberger.

10

University Lady

Since the university she got into was in Budapest, Rika continued to live at home, but after turning eighteen, she became unwilling to tolerate her mother's attempts to control her. The repeated flexing of her independence led to frequent arguments, in which Rika, inhibited and tongue tied, was unable to counter her mother's criticisms, and then spent the following sleepless nights feverishly constructing in her mind eloquent ripostes that evaporated in sober daylight before they could be utilised in the next confrontation.

In the new environment of the English degree course she started going out with a fellow student in her year, Atilla, a boy from Debrecen. He was duly introduced to Rika's mother, who voiced no objections to him. And for a while the skirmishes between mother and daughter became lighter.

During the second year of university Rika was making her way home with Atilla. It was a Saturday night, after the last bus, and the streets were deserted. They had been to a gig at one of the university's student residences, where in the full-to-overflowing dining hall, occasionally serving as a concert venue, the first Hungarian prog-rock band, Syrius, performed.

Rika was still spellbound. In the last few hours swaying to the sounds and swigging cheap wine, she had the impression that this music expressed what she felt and wanted from life. Being free, unbound by conventions, open to unexpected possibilities. She was especially thrilled by the mesmerising, jazz-flavoured solos of the brilliant saxophone player.

As they were walking along Rákóczi Road, Atilla told her what he knew about the band. 'Apparently, they couldn't get a recording contract here. They were considered too elitist. But now that their first album had come out in Australia, Hungaroton is very keen to buy *The Devil's Masquerade* and issue it.'

They reached Rika's house. As it was past eleven the street door was locked and she had to ring the bell. After some ten minutes' wait the morose, yawning caretaker shuffled into view, in a coat over his pyjamas, and opened the door. Atilla said good night and continued on his own journey back to his hall of residence. Rika slipped some money into the caretaker's hand and while climbing the stairs to the second floor she wondered why can't the residents be given their own house keys.

She let herself into their flat, but didn't switch on the light in the hall, in case the chink of brightness under her mother's door woke her up. She could easily feel her way to her own room without it.

Out of the darkness suddenly the white-gowned figure of her mother, like a wrathful ghost, materialised.

'Where have you been? What time do you call this?'

'Oh! We went to the E-klub, for a Syrius concert. I've told you.'

'I've been worried sick, I could get no sleep. Do you know what time it is? I was on the point of calling the police.'

'It's just past one, and you knew I was with Atilla. We walked back together. You didn't have to wait up.'

'You might show some consideration for your mother. But, no, you're an arrogant *university lady*, you don't care if your mother is losing sleep and worried to death about you.'

Rika thought, if she hadn't gone to university her mother would be just as dissatisfied with that. But she could think of no reply that wouldn't aggravate the situation. As she opened the door to her own room she heard her mother's parting shot.

'Even though you're a *university lady* now, you still have to heed your mother'.

The call went round among Rika's classmates at the university, 'We shall be meeting at the Petőfi statue at midday on 15th of March.'

'It will be just a commemoration, we don't want a political demonstration,' added János, one of the organisers.

Assembling on the anniversary of the 1848 revolution at the statue of one of its leaders – the romantic poet who died in the ensuing war of independence against the ruling Habsburgs – had become a regular event in Budapest in the last four years since the Paris *événements* and the Prague Spring.

'Is it permitted? It's not an official holiday. Will the police be there?' asked one of the vacillating students.

'The government dare not ban these gatherings', said János, 'the events of 1848 have such an iconic significance in the national consciousness. But I'm certain the police will keep a close watch on the square. After all, it was a demonstration at that spot that sparked off the 1956 uprising.'

A few days later Rika got off the bus on Kossuth Street, where she and her classmates, including Atilla, had agreed to meet. The weather was mild for early spring and she wore a short jacket, glad that she could dispense with her heavy winter coat.

They saw from a distance that the road leading to the Elizabeth Bridge, their direct access, was blocked off further on by police barricades, so they weaved through the smaller side streets and crossing Váci Street circled round to the north side of 15th of March Square. On the way everybody pinned onto their coats the cockades Rika had made in the red-white-green national colours.

Arriving at the edge of the crowd they could hear in the distance somebody declaiming the famous lines of Petőfi's *National Song. Shall we be slaves or men set free / that is the question, answer me!*

The crowd responded passionately, with the refrain of the poem every schoolchild knew by heart. *By all the gods of Hungary we hereby swear / that we the yoke of slavery no more shall wear.* Rika and her friends joined in the chanting, moving gradually closer to the statue in the centre.

After the second repeat of the refrain, police loudspeakers started up on the south side of the square. 'This is an illegal assembly. You are breaking the law. Disperse immediately!' they ordered again and again.

Drowned out by the loudspeakers, the crowd had fallen into a shocked silence of seconds before the confused shouting and running started.

Rika scrambled onto a street bench and caught a glimpse of the long-haired performer of the poem being dragged away from the plinth of the statue. Police on horseback were zigzagging about, clearing the square, not sparing their batons to get people to leave. She saw that some of the students were pursued towards the fenced-in Roman ruins in front of the church and, beaten with truncheons, tumbled a couple of metres into the sunken area.

One of her classmates shouted, 'Come on, let's get out of here! Along the Danube Promenade, towards the Chain Bridge! Once we get across, we'll be safe.'

Rika tried to jump down from the bench and run at the same time, only to fall to the ground with a twisted ankle and a yelp. Her brain registered a searing pain and a paralysing fear, as she saw the stampeding demonstrators getting closer.

'Don't leave me!' she shouted towards her departing friends.

The next moment Atilla was back and pulled her to her feet. She couldn't put any weight on her injured foot, so to get out of the square quickly he gathered her up and carried her to a safe side alley. From there, slowly hobbling, she made her way home with his help.

In the following days they learnt at the university that a number of the demonstrators got injured. There was also a circulating story, which may or may not have been true.

A couple of students, from the year above them, were walking through the nearby streets, talking and laughing, right after the square was ordered to be cleared. The police asked what they were laughing at.

'Is laughing forbidden too?' one of the students asked. Which apparently got both of them arrested.

Rika was at home one evening with her mother, just the two of them, without Gábor around or Grandpa László to stay. It was their shared name-day and they celebrated with a bottle of cherry brandy.

The sugary sips felt harmless, but their stealthily disinhibiting effects soon showed. Mária confided to her daughter her dissatisfaction about the relationship with Uncle Géza. 'He's so boring, all he wants to do now is to work. He's not taking me out anywhere. When I go over to his place, we just stay in his flat.'

As the level of liquor in the bottle went down, Mária's unburdening went up a level.

'His ... his ... some of his habits are so off-putting. You know, for years I've tried to get him to shower before bed, esp ... espesh ... especially in summer. He doesn't get the hint.'

'And when we're in bed, ... it's not much to speak of, ... he just rolls on and then off ... when he can do it at all.'

Rika wanted her mother to stop, but Mária continued, 'It's not like that with Bence, it's really exciting with him.'

Rika almost choked on her cheese puff. 'You mean Bence, the miner, who rented a room at Aunty Rózsi's last month?'

'Yes. He knows what a woman wants. And he's not the only one to find me attractive.'

This confession, so uncharacteristic of her mother,

prompted the by now equally unrestrained Rika to ask, 'But ...
but, do you miss that side of things, ... I mean ... do you miss ...
sex?'

It was a daring question, as they had never had any
conversations about sex, a subject her mother had always
avoided.

'Uhm, ... yeees, ... I do ...', Mária answered haltingly, then
added, 'Rózsi's right, I don't have to put up with boring old
Géza.'

Waking up the next morning with a headache Rika could
only remember the most surprising of her mother's confessions.
When the intimate confidences were not repeated or even
mentioned, Rika concluded that Mária had either forgotten or
regretted them.

After the collapse of their marriage, Tamás sent, as promised, the
child maintenance money to Mária every month without fail.
But over the years the monthly amounts stayed the same and did
not reflect his salary increases, nor did the children of his first
marriage benefit from the substantial yearly bonuses he received.

Eventually Mária learnt that Tamás had been cheating
them out of the lawful amount for years. She wanted to get legal
redress and have the money deducted at source from her ex-
husband's salary. Tamás tried to wriggle out of the official
arrangements again and asked to see his ex-wife to discuss the
matter before she went to court.

Hoping for an ally at the confrontation Mária asked her
daughter to be present at the meeting. This surprised Rika. In
the past year she had frequently clashed with her mother, who

hadn't given up exerting control over her daughter. But recently Rika had also been on friendly terms with her father. She told him about what she got up to with her friends at uni and about the tense atmosphere at home. From his reactions she felt that he was sympathetic. She was in a quandary: her father was clearly in the wrong, so her mother needed her support, but her father also seemed an ally in her battles with her mother.

Turning up at the flat in Thököly Road, Tamás was taken aback by finding his daughter also present. Undeterred by this, he skilfully steered the discussion away from his own wrongdoing and started off by attacking his ex-wife.

'You question whether I have done my duty as a father. But what kind of a mother are you?'

Before Maria could stammer out a response, he continued, 'Do you even know where your daughter has been when she comes home at one in the morning? Do you know the kind of things she gets up to?'

Then he tried to plead financial hardship, 'I have a new marriage now and my wife is expecting our first child. I will soon have another family to support'.

And finally, 'If you give up the legal action, I promise that from now on I'll pay the correct amount every month and will send extra when I get a bonus'.

Mária could hardly get a word in edgeways and was unable to counter her ex-husband's aggressive arguments. She was outmanoeuvred by him and in the end agreed to his suggestions again.

Rika felt ill-used by both of her parents, but especially let down by her father who betrayed her confidences.

The amount of the monthly payments from Tamás did increase, but no share of his yearly bonuses ever came. Mária was too browbeaten to try to fight once more and the maintenance payments came to an end naturally when Rika finished university.

One evening in late April Rika was working in her room, struggling with an essay due to be submitted in a couple of days. The weather was unseasonably warm and her windows were open, but she had pulled the shutters down to be shielded from prying eyes in the house opposite. In the next room of the flat the blaring sound of the TV suddenly got extinguished; her mother had gone to sleep. Outside, the last buses and trams had been and gone, only the occasional car-noise or the footsteps of homecoming residents broke the silence of Thököly Road.

She was engrossed in honing her arguments on the essay topic 'The English are empirical and sensuous'. She hadn't noticed that the soundscape of the street had changed, until a grinding, grating noise had broken into her consciousness. What's that? What's happening? She pushed out the lower half of the shutters and peeped down into the street.

In the middle of the road along the tram-tracks there was a line of tanks moving slowly towards the left. The creaking caterpillar treads were crunching on the rails and the cobblestones. There was nothing else on the street, it was entirely emptied of people and traffic. The barrels of some of the advancing tanks were sweeping from side to side as if trying to ward off possible attacks.

Rika watched the procession, half-leaning out of her

window, taking care not to be seen behind the shutter. It was a surreal scene. Was this the opening gambit of some kind of invasion? She noticed that at the traffic lights two blocks away the file of tanks was turning into the road that lead to Heroes' Square.

After the last of the sinister metal beasts disappeared from sight and the rumbling and rattling died away, she suddenly realised that tomorrow was the 1st of May and the tanks were going to be part of the military parade. They were just moving to the site ahead of time to be ready on May Day.

The mystery was solved. But it felt no less bizarre for that.

During the academic year Rika's boyfriend, Atilla, lodged at the university's halls of residence. As Rika still lived at home this posed a problem for their love life. In his hall visitors, especially those of the opposite sex, had to sign in at the reception and sign out when leaving before ten in the evening. Nobody was allowed to stay overnight.

Atilla always had a cleverly devised solution to an undesirable situation. On weekends when his room mate had gone home Rika arrived at the hall on Friday afternoon and duly signed in. Shortly after 10pm Atilla went down and signed her out, having told the friendly receptionist who just arrived for the night shift that they forgot to do so when she had left half an hour earlier. Rika then actually left the building the next morning, unnoticed, as people going out at that time were not monitored.

This ruse worked without a hitch for several months.

One Saturday morning while waiting for Atilla in the

entrance lobby on her way out she was approached by a be-suited, middle-aged man, the Director of the Hall. He invited her into his office and questioned her.

Rika was taken completely by surprise and didn't have a prepared cover story. She didn't agree with the rules, because she thought they were pointless. While she had a vague idea of the consequences of being caught, she simply couldn't lie and as good as admitted that she'd stayed the night.

The result was that Atilla was expelled from the hall of residence with immediate effect.

Rika felt it was all her fault. Her thoughtless and naively rebellious stance with the Director was irresponsible, empty posturing at his expense. She had to find a solution.

She approached her mother. 'Atilla's lost his place in the hall of residence. Can he come and stay with us?'

'What's happened?' asked Mária.

'Oh, there was some administrative cock-up', lied Rika. 'He's staying with classmates now, where he can't study and he'll lose his grant. My room is large enough for two. Until he gets his place back'.

Mária agreed. The camping bed was set up, 'hidden' behind a large writing desk bisecting Rika's room and Atilla moved in.

Two days later arriving home from a late tutorial Rika found him packing up his things in their room.

'Are you leaving already? Did you hear ... did you get your place back?'

'No, nothing like that,' he shook his head, trying to cram more textbooks into his suitcase. 'Your mother asked me to leave.'

Rika stormed out to the kitchen and confronted her mother, 'What's happened? You said Atilla could stay and now you kick him out, when you know he has nowhere to go! Why?'

'Your grandfather is coming to stay tomorrow and he wouldn't like you two sharing a room.'

'That's rubbish! Grandpa likes Atilla, and he doesn't care, he doesn't really understand what's going on!'

'Yes, he does. You know he's old fashioned, he's not used to modern ways.'

'That's not true! You are just using Grandpa as a pretext, because *you* don't want it! And you did it so sneakily, asking Atilla behind my back! Because you knew ... you knew that if you ask him face-to-face he won't be able to refuse!'

In his room next to the kitchen Gábor heard the shouted arguments and tried to weigh in on his sister's side, but they could not change their mother's mind.

Rika returned to her room, 'You don't have to leave just because my mother said so. Anyway, where can you go?'

'I haven't thought, ... but I don't want to stay, ... I don't feel welcome.'

Charging back to the kitchen, Rika declared: 'If Atilla has to leave, if you kick him out, I will go too.'

'If that's what you want, I won't stop you,' was Mária's only reaction.

Rika quickly packed a case for herself and walked out of the flat with Atilla. Mária watched them without saying a word.

They roamed the city with suitcases in hand. During a long spun-out cheap meal they tried to think where they could stay.

After eleven they emerged from the closing restaurant into the rainy night with no solution found.

They had to find overnight shelter. Hotels, even if they could afford them, were not an option for an unmarried couple. Waiting rooms at railway stations could have been an alternative, but they were regularly patrolled by the police, looking for vagrants.

The only places to hide in plain sight were night entertainment venues. They sat out a few hours in a couple of bars, over live music and drinks with inflated, with-music prices, pretending enjoyment and fighting sleepiness, their suitcases stashed away and coats drying in the cloakroom.

After these 'night clubs' closed their doors it was six in the morning, the start of the working day, when it was no longer suspicious to walk around carrying suitcases.

They took the bus to the university, showered in the basement sport facilities and downed strong coffees before their first class at eight. No matter how tired they were, they couldn't afford to miss lectures, since their grants depended on regular attendance. Following a brief afternoon catnap in the library they were faced again with the problem of finding somewhere to stay.

Rika had an idea. 'Grandpa László was going to stay for days in Thököly Road, perhaps while he's there we can sleep in his flat in Albertfalva . I just need to contact my cousin, Laci. He's living with Grandpa.'

There was no phone at Grandpa's flat and Laci, an aspiring sportsman, spent long hours in training. Rika and Atilla had no choice but to turn up at the flat in the evening. Laci answered the door after ten to find his cousin and her boyfriend on the doorstep. He could not turn them away.

By the following evening Laci had a change of heart. 'Grandpa is coming back earlier than planned, you have to leave.'

Rika wondered what happened. Was Laci pressurised by his mother and Mária, his godmother, to stop helping the rebels? Did he comply because he didn't want to jeopardise his permanent stay with Grandpa?

Resuming their search for shelter, Atilla heard of a spare room in the home of a classmate whose mother had gone away for a short holiday. The classmate invited them to move in straight away and they had a few days' respite from wandering and caught up on sleep and university course work.

This refuge, however, also proved temporary when the mother of their friend returned. She was willing to rent the room on a long term basis to Atilla, but not to both of them, not to an unmarried couple.

To Atilla, this was the least worst solution to his predicament. The rent – though more than the subsidized residence hall fee – was reasonable and he did not have to give up or pause his studies.

To Rika, it was no solution: she had nobody to turn to for help and no alternative but to go back to Thököly Road.

Rika let herself into the flat in the afternoon. Gábor was already back from school and really chuffed to see his sister. Rika parked her suitcase in the hall and over a cup of tea in Gábor's room they exchanged their news of the past week. She told him about the failed attempts she and Atilla had in finding somewhere to stay, including the episode with Laci.

'Nobody told me what was going on,' said Gábor. 'I think they met up, at Aunt Blondie's. I heard mother on the phone, but she'd said nothing to me.'

An hour later they heard their mother's key in the front door, then her footsteps into the kitchen, then the clatter of something being heated up on the stove, and finally the closing of the front door as she left the flat and went over to her friend Rózsi.

Mária had seen the suitcase in the hall and could hear her children talking in Gábor's den behind the curtain, but pretended that she had seen or heard nothing. Rika, feeling defeated and humiliated by having to come home, did not call out to her mother. Gábor, out of sympathy, also stayed silent.

Before her mother returned from Aunt Rózsi's, Rika went into her own room, unpacked her suitcase and soon fell into an exhausted sleep. The next morning after her mother had left for work she took the bus to the university and attended her morning lectures, as usual.

From this time on Rika avoided her mother, if she could. She moved about in the flat, with brief forays into the kitchen or to Gábor's den, when her mother was out. Otherwise she kept to her room or went out and came home late. Mother and daughter never discussed or even referred to what had happened. Mária waited for contrition and asking for forgiveness from her daughter. Rika refused to see returning home as a capitulation or a vindication of her mother's, in her view, unpardonable behaviour. There was no way back even to their previous, already far from perfect, relationship. Communications between them became whittled down to a coolly polite exchange of 'Good morning' if they met accidentally in the hall or the kitchen.

During the summer vacation before their last year at university Atilla went home and kept in touch with Rika by regular phone-calls. In the middle of August he told her that his father had committed suicide.

Ever since they started going out Rika had felt that Atilla was reluctant to talk about his background, always clamming up when asked about his parents or siblings. From an unguarded remark she had gathered that someone in his family had mental health problems, which for her explained his secrecy, so she didn't probe further.

He was not more communicative even now, but she thought it insensitive to ask questions. She tried to offer him some comfort. 'I'm so sorry about your Dad ... what a tragedy ... I know I haven't met him, but I'd like to come to the funeral. If you don't mind.'

'No need. We just want to have it over quickly. No outsiders.'

His last words stung. So that's what he thought of her. But that's surely the result of shock and shame and grief and pain, she shouldn't get offended, she reasoned with herself.

'I'll stay here after the funeral to support my mother and sister. I've asked the university if I could suspend my studies for a year,' he ended the call.

In their less and less frequent phone-calls over the next few months he reported that he'd found a job in local government, reconnected with his friends from school and abandoned the idea of finishing university. Rika tried to persuade him not to give up his studies, talked about plodding on with her course, and recounted the news of their friends and of her family.

But in the end the phone conversations were not sufficient to span the distance of their drifting-apart lives. In April he told her he was going to marry his childhood sweetheart, who was expecting their child.

Rika was not entirely surprised, but was deeply hurt. She had thought they loved each other, so how could he switch his affections from one person to another so quickly? Maybe his feelings were not as strong as hers. Or did he carry on with his first love all the time he lived in Budapest? Then she realised that his father's death was a catalyst for totally upending his life and she didn't feel she could berate him. Instead, she expressed congratulations for his wedding and the baby, and hung up.

11

Poet as a Young Man

The fourteenth birthday. That crucial point, the Rubicon. And the ultimate weapon his mother always hurled at him to close down an argument.

'You can choose to go and live with your father when you're fourteen, but while you live under my roof, you do as you are told!'

Gábor had heard it so many times, it was etched in his mind. He had to take up the challenge, if only for his self-respect. He didn't want to be treated like a child. Why couldn't his mother consider what he wanted, why couldn't she take his views into account, why did she always want to dictate to him? When he already saw things more clearly than she did.

By the time he managed to bring about his escape he was closer to sixteen. To the clashes at home were added the ones at school: at the *gimnázium*, which his sister had also attended, where he felt they regarded him as an inferior version. Where Huber, that stupid, petty-minded German teacher, had it in for him. That arsehole sensed the intellectual challenge to his authority and could only deal with it by trying to fail him and getting the school to exclude him.

When his mother couldn't – or more likely, wouldn't – stand up for him against the school, Gábor had to turn to his father. He finally had to make good on the many promises he'd held out to his son since the divorce. Like taking Gábor with them to Cuba after he'd married Nadia. As if there had been any chance of removing a ten-year-old boy from a mother's custody. His father must have known it wasn't going to happen, but was still stringing him along.

When Gábor told his mother he wanted to go and live with his father, she had no choice but to contact her ex-husband and tell him their son's wish. Mária and Tamás discussed the matter, and although neither of them was keen on this change, they couldn't very well object to it.

Tamás came to collect his son and Gábor moved in with his father and his wife. Éva, wife number three, five years older than Gábor, was expecting a baby, his half brother or sister. She'd had a number of miscarriages before Tamás took her to a famous gynaecologist. She was still in danger of losing the baby, so she was resting at home all day.

Gábor slept on the sofa in their one bedroom flat, travelled an hour longer to school and back every day, and spent the afternoons with Éva, while his father was at work. He read his first poems to her. She was impressed by his intellect and treated him as her equal. His life prior to living next to her seemed to disappear from his mind. She filled his world. Her pregnant curves filled his dreams.

At night while his father snored in the bedroom next door, Gábor lay on the sofa and fantasized about Éva. In the morning he smuggled his sticky pyjamas into the washing machine, trying to hide the evidence. He imagined running away with her. He wasn't sure if she would be willing – he hadn't dared to confess his feelings to her – but he wanted to press her to get a divorce. He had no consideration for his father. Why, his father didn't think about his children when he left all those years ago to pursue the love of his life. This might be my only chance of a little personal happiness, thought Gábor.

After a few months of living at his father's Gábor was suddenly taken back to Thököly Road. Carted back to his mother, like a piece of luggage, he felt. Without reason or explanation. Or rather, the explanation was given to his mother, not to him. That it was a stressful situation for his father, now that his wife was expecting a child, to live in that small flat, all three of them together. Blah, blah, blah. His father knew how to spin things.

The truth was that he was rejected. Again. By both of his parents. Didn't his father tell him that his mother hadn't really wanted to have him in the first place? Apparently, when she discovered she was pregnant with him she wanted an abortion. Nobody wanted him. He must be worthless. That's why nobody wanted him. Was he even normal? Or was he defective, damaged? Had he been dropped on his head after birth? He would have to ask Rika, she would tell him, even if nobody else dared to admit the truth.

Gábor was back in Thököly Road, with his mother and sister,

back to square one. To prevent his mother forgetting his rebellion, he took over the room that used to be his father's workroom. It still had his desk and many of his tools and instruments in it, as he'd left them behind years ago. The way to the kitchen was through this room, where in a previous era the maid would have slept. He barricaded himself at the larger, inner part of the room, away from the window, behind a cupboard and a curtain.

He didn't mind that not much light permeated into his room-within-a-room. He didn't keep to conventional times of sleeping and waking, other than what he absolutely had to for school. He read and wrote poems by lamplight and made a point of not staying awake for mealtimes. Much to his mother's annoyance. And when his mother had gone to bed, he would raid the fridge or eat up the leftovers he could find.

When somebody went through to the kitchen, he regarded it as showing insufficient consideration for him, as an unreasonable disturbance of his privacy. It was only his mother, though, who was guilty of that. When Rika came to talk with him, she usually opened the door quietly and knocked on the door jamb before pulling aside the curtain.

Moving into his father's abandoned workroom brought Gábor back memories of the days when the two of them were tinkering with radios. His seven-year-old self became curious about what his father was doing in his den and fascinated by the weird and wonderful instruments there. One with a screen on which snake-like, luminous green waves chased each other or the one which emitted an airy, whining sound. They all had strange names: voltmeter, generator, oscilloscope, amplifier. It was like a circus in which his father, the main performer, pulled off unusual feats, including the magic trick of letting the electric current go through him and remain unharmed.

Gábor realized that as a child he idolized his father, regarding him as infallible and the font of all knowledge, and not just in his professional field. When adults asked him which football team he supported, he would unthinkingly reply 'Fradi', and when asked why, he would say 'because Apukám, my Daddy is a fan of them'. He was ashamed of this now, and thought his childhood self should have been more thinking, more questioning, and less accepting or parroting of other people's views.

He gradually explored and made his own all the things he found in the room. Listening to the tapes that went with the big Grundig reel-to-reel tape recorder, he discovered a recording his father made, as it happened, while advising a friend on the phone about radio-repair and simultaneously *educating* his son, by casually administering a beating for a minor prank. The 'Apuka spanks Gabika' tape became a symbol of his father's relationship – or non-relationship – with him.

After their mother got involved with the lawyer who handled her divorce, she usually spent long weekends with him, staying at his flat or going away on short trips with him. She had said she didn't want to give Rika and Gábor a stepfather, that's why she wouldn't marry Uncle Géza. Gábor suspected that this was just an excuse, that she didn't really want to, perhaps because he was so much older than her or that she had grown wary of another marriage after her divorce.

Not that Uncle Géza was in a position to marry, anyway; he had a sick wife in a sanatorium in the Buda hills, whom he regularly visited. He was an OK guy, though, even if he gave such embarrassingly old fashioned and unsolicited advice as 'when you go courting, Gábor, don't forget to pull on the rubber', as if he were a father substitute. He enjoyed taking Rika out for an ice cream and liked being seen with her, and he was not at all in a hurry to correct people's assumptions that *she* was his girlfriend, not her mother.

One spring weekend Gábor was at home on his own, his mother away with Uncle Géza and Rika out with her boyfriend. He seized the opportunity of being alone in the flat and took his big speakers into Rika's room, which faced the street, and played his favourite Led Zeppelin and Jimi Hendrix tracks at full volume. He enjoyed not being told, for a change, to turn the volume down.

The windows were open all along Thököly Road in the warm Easter sunshine and one of the neighbours called the police. They couldn't find a responsible adult, so it became a major incident, and his mother got the summons to the police station later. She spun a story that her son fell asleep while revising. And her excuse why she wasn't there to keep an eye on a minor? She was away attending to her sick father. Of course, thought Gábor, she had to maintain the fictitious public image of the saintly, self-sacrificing mother and couldn't possibly admit that she was with her lover.

Talking of romantic attachments, Gábor couldn't complain. He had a succession of lovely girlfriends; the girls at school seemed to be drawn to his persona of the melancholy poet and long-haired rebel. Shy Márta, independent-minded Rachel, sensitive Andrea, feisty Erika. He spoke with the current one on the phone for hours when his mother was out, his velvety tone of voice reciting his poems was his most seductive tool. In the summer he took advantage of green outdoor spaces by the Danube for amorous trysts with his latest girl. Though none of them allowed him to go all the way.

He still had to go to school, however much he hated it. Though his father's talk with Huber had eased the pressure on him in the German classes, he repeatedly clashed with the teachers of other subjects, who also threatened to fail him, as he didn't prepare for classes or do his homework.

One day in the Scientific Socialism class the teacher asked Gábor to summarise what they'd learnt in the previous lesson. 'What is the difference between the form of socialism that currently exists and socialism that will evolve eventually?'

Gábor knew full well that the question was about the doctrine that socialism will naturally develop into communism, when people's class consciousness was advanced enough. But he chose to answer cheekily, 'The difference is that socialism that exists doesn't work and socialism that works doesn't exist.'

The joke wasn't his own, it had been doing the rounds in the school for weeks. As he uttered the last word, his classmates sniggered and the teacher flew from the front of the class to Gábor's desk and slapped him hard. 'How dare you... you arrogant little sod!

The class first froze, then erupted into a protest, 'But Comrade Teacher, what about a rational scientific discussion?'

'The theory and principles of Scientific Socialism are not open to debate', countered the teacher, before storming out of the classroom.

Despite the unanimous outcry of the class, Comrade Forgács, the deputy head of the school and an eminent Party member, was not dismissed or disciplined for hitting a pupil.

Seeing his twice-yearly results during the *gimnázium* Gábor gradually realised that he was unlikely to get into university. So why should he bother with home-works and tests, or worry about irrelevant subjects and exams? With minimal effort he'd just about scraped though the *érettségi* and he was finally free of school. He felt liberated. No more coercion, no further need to conform.

Since he was not continuing in formal education, he had to find a job within a month after finishing school. Nobody was allowed to be longer without work. Everybody had to have a place of employment recorded in their ID document or they could be branded a *közveszélyes munkakerülő*. And to be a work-avoider and as such a danger to the public, was a punishable offence, a crime.

He took on a series of short lived jobs: in a bookshop, where he clashed with the incompetent manager; as a land surveyor's assistant during an unusually cold, freezing winter; in a warehouse for electrical equipment, a job his father got him through his connections, which Gábor resented and eventually quit for the same reason.

He became conscious of the passing of time and marked his nineteenth birthday with a poem. *As if a clock / were ticking inside me / As if under orders I placed / the same things again / into the basket of today / and carried them to the tower / on the spiral staircase of dreams / to be digested by time.*

His next job as a postman unexpectedly turned out to be the ideal occupation for him, at least for the time being. Though the postbag was heavy, with hobby magazines and weeklies in addition to the regular mail, he had no boss barking orders over his shoulder and he could finish work around eight in the morning and then he was free and could spend the rest of the day as he wished.

Their brother, Andris, was born and a year later a baby sister, Viki. Gábor and Rika went to see their father's new family frequently, playing with their half-siblings and witnessing their first steps and words. Éva, the young mother, was blooming and Gábor found her more attractive than ever.

Keeping it a secret, even from Rika, he started visiting Éva alone when his father was at work. While the children had their afternoon nap, in the kitchen-diner Gábor and Éva had regular heart-to-heart conversations. His passion for her was re-awakened.

He offered her his poems, flowers of his intellect, bouquets to impress her. Baffled by their dense impenetrability Éva picked out a couple of the simpler lines – *From afar my voice runs to you for an embrace ... my heart is full of you* – and was flattered. 'I've never had poems written to me.'

That's not all my poems are about, darted through his

mind, but the moment drove the thought away. Turning to look at her sitting next to him on the bench he suddenly felt propelled towards her as if physically pushed by an invisible force or pulled by an irresistible magnet. At the last second what looked like an attack became a kiss. His mouth touched hers and she responded, hungrily. The eagerness of her reaction amazed and ignited him, he was on fire, unquenchable.

'Oh, Éva, I love you, I've been dreaming of this so long ... do you know how much ... '

She silenced him with her lips and pulling him up from the bench, lead him to the living room. Shedding their clothes on the way they only just made it as far as the sofa.

It was his first time. He fumbled, he was clumsy, but *she* knew what to do, *she* was experienced. He came all too soon, but was ready again in no time. Her gorgeous body a permanent trigger.

This sudden burst into sexual intimacy left him utterly intoxicated. He couldn't get enough of her, grabbing every moment he could spend with her alone. He felt his life had finally started. The world had got onto the right track.

Months later, as they were making love on the living room carpet he become aware of little Andris, who, having woken up from his afternoon nap, toddled over from the other room and was now patting his naked bottom, muttering, 'Gabika's botty, Gabika's botty.'

Éva pushed Gábor off and after pulling on her tracksuit bottoms, took her son back to his bed. 'Gabi and I were just playing. But you should still be sleeping, like Viki, it's not time to wake up yet.'

This episode gave Éva a sobering jolt. 'We'd better cool things down for a while. What if Andris blurts something out? What if his baby chatter gives away to your father what we've been up to? I'm really afraid,' she said.

'Well, then at least everything will be out in the open. No more pretence. You should leave him and get a divorce and live with me.

'Are you mad? I can't leave him. And what about Andris and Viki? They would lose their father.'

'I can adopt them,' suggested Gábor.

'That's absurd. And what would we live on? Your wages as a postman?

'You're such a hypocrite. I know you don't love him. You just want to stick with a convenient situation even if it means living a lie. You've got too used to all the things he gives you ... do you know what that makes you? ...'

Gábor bit his tongue, not wanting to say out loud what he had come to think of her. His dreams have turned out to be impossible, his hopes have turned to ashes.

He threw himself into writing poems, reading voraciously everything that interested him, and immersing himself in studying German, again, now without compulsion from school, in his own way, with an intensive focus. Within a few months he was able to read German poetry in the original. He discovered Rilke, who became his favourite poet, and he translated his *Duino Elegies*.

One night station-hopping on the radio he came across some foreign words that charmed him with their lilting melody.

He was instantly smitten and decided to learn Swedish. Without a course book or a teacher, armed only with a German-Swedish dictionary – there was no Hungarian version to be had – he made use of radio programmes and any printed material he could lay his hands on. He hit upon a method of learning by analysing sentences word by word, working out the meaning from the context and deducing the grammar rules.

It became his passion, his obsession. An intellectual challenge, a way of keeping his brain exercised and, he had to admit, proving his former teachers wrong about his capabilities. He sought out the new Ingmar Bergman films shown in the art cinema in Budapest. These were subtitled as they were not popular enough to be dubbed into Hungarian – the standard treatment of foreign films – and he saw each several times until he'd learnt the dialogue by heart and the phrases become part of his vocabulary.

He usually got home from delivering the post after his mother had gone to work. He had breakfast with Rika before she left for her classes at the university. The two of them cooked porridge and drank tea with milk, food habits considered strange and eccentric in Hungary. Just a couple of those things Rika had introduced him to after her holiday in England.

Funnily enough, at the time he didn't think that her first visit to the West had left a strong impression on her. He thought she'd only gone because reading for an English degree she had to. He realised now how wrong he was. That holiday increased her interests in all things English and he had also become infected by her enthusiasm.

They had often talked late into the night in his room: discussing politics and the state of the world, philosophising and speculating about the future of mankind in the light of the latest science fiction books they had both read.

He showed Rika his writings, fully aware that he was trying to get her approval, as he had always done, ever since they were small. She liked his poems, the spare wordings, the striking images and the unusual juxtapositions, while admitting that she sometimes didn't get the condensed metaphors. *I put my bed outside into the rain / so somebody may come for it.* 'What does it mean?' she asked.

This upset him terribly. If somebody who knew him as well as she did couldn't understand his poems, then what chance did he have with other people? She also remarked on his tendency towards gloom and pessimism, and came up with the teasing pun: *A mártír mért ír?* Why does the martyr write? This was a clever quip, he had to admit, even if not entirely appropriate.

Gábor, Rika and their mother now lived together in the flat, like a *ménage à trois* without the sex.

Since leaving school Gábor had effectively separated his daily domestic life from his mother's: blocked her various attempts to cook for him, to clean his room or to wash his clothes. Making it impossible for her to say, 'because I do all these things for you, you should do what I want'. He paid his share of the rent and the bills, and he conducted his life independently of her, just like a flat-sharer or a lodger would.

After Rika's own bust up with their mother, her way of coping with having to live at home had followed much same pattern as his, except with even less contact with their mother.

As Gábor and Rika grew closer to each other, Mária increasingly distanced herself from them both, and spent most of her time with her neighbour and bosom friend, Rózsi.

One late May a suitcase appeared in the hall on a chair next to the wardrobe. It's lid was propped open and the contents of it increased day after day, with towels, sandals, sun cream, swimsuit and summer clothes.

Gábor wisecracked, 'Our mother has started her urgent packing; it looks like she'll go on holiday in a month's time.'

But Mária hasn't said anything to her children until two weeks later, when on the evening before her departure she finally told them that she was going on a package holiday to Sochi with Rózsi.

While Gábor and Rika breathed a sigh of relief that for a week they will be free of the oppressive atmosphere in the flat, they were worried about the growing and, in their view, harmful influence Aunty Rózsi had on their mother.

12

Asylum Seeker?

In October 1976 the train from Dover pulled into London Victoria Station in steady rain and descending dusk. Off the train and through the barriers, Rika found herself on the concourse, disorientated and bewildered. So many people, hurrying in all directions, and confusing signs everywhere. The elation she felt after slipping through the Hungarian border had since been replaced by travel fatigue and helplessness. What should she do now? How to proceed from here? And more immediately, where could she sleep tonight?

Struggling through the crowds with her heavy suitcase she eventually spotted the neon sign of the Tourist Information kiosk. According to her guidebook, which she studied carefully on the last leg of her journey, that was the place to look for accommodation.

The dark-skinned lady behind the desk was friendly and helpful. After ringing around to several places, she found Rika a hotel room, at a slightly reduced rate because it was already quite late.

'You'll need to take the tube to Earl's Court, then it's a short walk from there. I'll draw you a map.' She explained to Rika, with motherly concern. 'And you'll need some change to buy the ticket from the machine. Have you got an underground where you come from, love? Bucharest, isn't it?'

'We have three metro lines' – Rika couldn't expect everybody to know what the capital of Hungary was, and felt she had to clarify – 'in Budapest.' 'And where can I find a Foreign Exchange Bureau?'

'Just over there, on the other side of the station.'

Rika thanked her and said goodbye.

'Have you got a brolly, love?' the lady remembered. 'You'll need it with the downpours we've been having. Mind you, the rain's welcome, after the scorching summer we've had.'

Before stepping out of the tube station and into the now heavy rain, Rika studied the Tourist Information lady's hand-drawn map. She had to memorise the route before setting out, because she wouldn't have a free hand to hold it. As she opened her umbrella, she thought how funny the lady imagined anybody would come to England without one.

Luckily the hotel on a street with an elegant-sounding name was not far away, but by the time she got there her arm felt ready to drop off from the weight of the suitcase, and her clothes were soaked through from the waist down.

Hotel Atenea was a white stuccoed building with a portico, one in a row of a dozen near-identical buildings, looking impressive in the street lights. The man at the reception asked for her passport and payment in advance before escorting her to the room. Rika followed him, dragging her suitcase down the narrow flight of steps. The barred window of the room in the basement overlooked something dark, that she could just about glimpse before the receptionist hurriedly drew the curtains on it. He explained to her how to light the gas fire and feed the meter with coins, showed her the shared bathroom, told her the time breakfast was served, then wished her good night and left.

Rika locked the door and explored her room. Pulling the curtain aside she could faintly make out a brick wall a couple of metres away. Inside, the wall underneath the window was marbled with mould and the paint was flaking off. The dingy central pendant light was seemingly dressed in pink Victorian bloomers. Covering the double bed was a candlewick bedspread, goose-poo-green in colour and unpleasant to the touch, and there were nylon sheets on the bed. How disgusting, she thought, what a depressing place.

Impulsive thoughts darted through her mind: that she may have made a huge mistake, that this attempt of hers to flee may have been foolhardy. If this was what she was escaping to, if this was a portent for the future, then maybe she should just admit defeat, turn around and go back. But the room had already been paid for and they had kept her passport, so she had to stay here for one night at least.

A shiver ran through her. She should get out of these wet clothes, have a hot shower and light the fire. She was exhausted and cold, and after a deeply upsetting departure and a long, stressful journey this was not the time to make a decision, she reasoned with herself. It may all look different in the morning, after a night's sleep.

Next morning the rain and the despondency of the previous night were replaced by a bright day and the recovered optimism of the rested. Her hotel room looked a little less depressing in the daylight, despite the discovery that she couldn't see the sky from her window, only the feet of passers-by on the pavement above. She reckoned she could put up with staying here for a few nights, since it was relatively cheap and she had to watch her money until she knew what would happen.

Rika had brought with her from Budapest an introductory letter to a Hungarian couple, friends of friends, and before doing anything else she contacted them, seeking their advice on how she could stay. Miklós & Judit left Hungary in 1966, under what circumstances, Rika did not know. Walking to their house in Finchley from the nearest tube station, Rika was impressed by the neighbourhood, the wide tree-lined streets and the big houses with gardens. They had done well for themselves, she thought.

Miklós tried to dissuade Rika. 'Why would you want to come here? You know that Britain's been called the sick man of Europe? You must have heard of the frequent strikes, and the IRA bombs, even in the centre of London! The economy is in crisis and inflation is 17%. It's no joke.' He also thought she was naive and had been frightened by something. 'I don't know what problems you've had at home, but believe me, defecting is not a solution.'

Rika, ashamed of her broken-up family, kept silent about her personal reasons and focused instead on the politics. 'Have you forgotten why you two came here ten years ago? The situation at home hasn't got any better, all those restrictions and repressions are still there, just more skilfully implemented, and dissent is definitely not tolerated.'

She suspected that they regarded her as 'Kádár's revenge' – as visitors or later arrivals sponging on earlier defectors from Hungary were usually referred to. Was this a case of settled immigrants trying to discourage others from following their examples, she wondered. Pulling up the ladder after them?

Judit, in contrast to her husband, was impressed by Rika's determination to disregard their warnings and stick to her plan. After some behind-the-scenes discussions between them, the couple suggested that Rika should go to the Home Office and claim political asylum as soon as possible. They rehearsed with Rika what she should say and Judit typed up her written application.

When Rika arrived at Lunar House there were already a couple of dozen people ahead of her in the queue. She had intended to be here at opening time, but could not afford to miss the pre-paid breakfast at the hotel and the complicated tube and train journey to Croydon took ages. While waiting for her number to come up on the electronic notice board she mentally rehearsed the reasoning in support of her application. When her turn came she went up to the counter, told the official behind the glass screen that she wanted to claim political asylum and handed over her application.

She was told that in order for her claim to be assessed she had to be interviewed. 'Do you want an interpreter?' she was asked. Afraid that her shortcomings in English might result in an unfavourable outcome, she answered yes.

The wait dragged across lunchtime, but she could not leave the room and risk missing the call to the interview. She was glad she had in her bag the sandwich she surreptitiously made at breakfast and smuggled out of the hotel.

In the middle of the afternoon she was finally called to the interview room. She found there two Immigration Officers, but no interpreter, whose non-appearance was not explained.

'Why would you want to leave your country and claim asylum in the UK?' one of the officers asked.

Rika elaborated on the arguments already stated in her written application. 'There is overall political control and no freedom in Hungary, as you know. People's lives are constantly surveilled. There are restrictions on travel and work. Recently a number of legislations have been published in a limited circulation legal journal, which are just waiting to be applied, and would further limit people's liberties. For example, if somebody is found without a place of employment for longer than a month, they could be sent to take up a particular job, whether it is suitable for them and whether they want it or not.'

She spoke passionately, her fluency in English boosted by emotions. The Immigration Officers listened impassively, made notes on what appeared to be her file and then left the room to confer with their superiors.

After a further short wait she had her answer: her application was rejected there and then. She was told she did not have sufficiently strong reasons to claim asylum: she had not been persecuted in her native country, nor could she demonstrate a well-founded fear of persecution if she had returned. When her tourist visa expired, she could and should go back, they suggested, the Hungarian authorities wouldn't know about her application and there would be no adverse consequences for her.

The rejection came accompanied by the notice of the right of appeal against the decision, and detailed notes about where to get assistance with preparing an appeal should she decide to lodge one.

On the way back to Central London she mulled over what had just happened. It was not an outcome she had envisaged. She was upset and disappointed, but not entirely disheartened. She had lost a battle, but not yet the whole war, she reasoned, she had to continue the fight. Wasn't the information that accompanied the decision – about the possibility of an appeal – a hint of what she needed to do?

Accordingly, the next day she contacted the Immigrants Advisory Service, where the lawyer assigned to her case asked Rika to summarise the arguments for the submission in her own words.

After a day and night of assiduous dictionary-thumbing in her hotel room Rika came up with two strands of thoughts as the basis for her appeal.

Firstly, how can you tell somebody they have no reason to escape from behind the Iron Curtain, when in the West people know how awful life is there, under Soviet domination, with general repression and dismal living conditions.

Secondly, she pointed out that if somebody had indeed been persecuted in their own country and would therefore be eligible for asylum, that person would certainly not be in the position to travel to another country and claim political asylum there.

The next day she handed the lawyer, Mrs Choudhury, her handwritten notes, expecting them to be dismissed as useless. After all, she thought, she had not been persecuted in Hungary, which seemed to her to be the only legitimate basis for challenging the Home Office's decision. Her arguments – which, if honest, she was quietly proud of – could be judged too emotional and beside the point, possibly even arrogant. However, Mrs Choudhury said that she would prepare the formal appeal on the basis of Rika's reasoning and submit it in the proper legal form.

A week later a letter arrived at Hotel Atenea addressed to Rika. When the receptionist handed it to her and she saw that it was sent from the Home Office, for a moment she froze in fear. Are they going to send her back? She couldn't slide her trembling fingers under the flap and in her haste she almost tore the envelope in half. Then, she stopped herself. Why be in such a hurry to read the bad news?

13

On the Home Front

The morning when Rika walked out of the flat in Thököly Road for the last time, Gábor strolled home from the railway station after seeing his sister off on her train journey to England. Although he had known for months about her plan and the preparations, it suddenly hit him that they might not see each other again.

He hoped she would succeed, yet wished she hadn't gone. How bereft he felt after her departure only dawned on him when during the following days he noticed himself *not* finishing off the jointly purchased bag of porridge oats, their breakfast staple of the last few months. Was he saving it, was he unconsciously waiting for her return?

A couple of weeks later he collected two letters from the downstairs postbox. One for him and one for their mother. Gábor recognised Rika's handwriting on the envelopes, but the return address was the name of an official organisation. This lead him to assume that on arrival in England Rika was put in a holding *lager*, just like some earlier defectors and escapees from

Hungary were believed to have been. The few vague details in her letter did nothing to dispel his imaginings.

He brought the other letter to their mother's attention when she came home from work, and suggested to her that she should write to Rika. But Mária didn't see her daughter's letter as a conciliatory opening, and dismissed it with the comment, 'I have no reply to such an arrogant letter.'

Gábor was the only person Rika kept in touch with from London. Correspondence between them were prompt and frequent to start with, gradually changing from weekly to monthly, before switching later on from letters to cassette-tapes. He then regularly fed news of his sister to their seemingly uninterested parents.

As it happened there was no official inquiry into Rika's defection after it became obvious that she would not return. Nobody came to question her mother and brother about their role in her departure and about their knowledge of it. It may have been because Rika was in between jobs, so there was no personnel manager or immediate superior who would have alerted the authorities when she did not turn up at work after her holiday. Or it may have been because, as a poet had put it, the fabric of the law always unravels somewhere.

A few months after Rika's departure Gábor moved into his sister's vacated room beside their mother's. This space was twice as big as his room-within-a-room next to the kitchen, had a street facing window and was not a thoroughfare to another room. This increased proximity soon led to fresh confrontations between mother and son, the source which was Mária's recent association with a young man.

Gyuri was one of the long-term lodgers of Rózsi, a neighbour and Mária's best friend. Having finishing his technical secondary school with a qualification as an electrician, Gyuri came up to Budapest from his small village in the north-east of the country to work in a factory. He shared a room in Rózsi's flat with three of his work mates and when they didn't go home to their families in the weekends they socialized with their landlady and her friend.

Despite the age difference, Mária and Gyuri became involved romantically and he started spending the nights in Mária's room.

Gábor was outraged. 'This boy is younger than me,' he wrote to Rika, 'what is our Mother doing with him?'

Examining his own motives, Gábor could not escape the suspicion that he was jealous. After all, he'd read Freud and knew about the Oedipus complex. But as someone who didn't conform to moral conventions himself, on the surface he could only object to his mother failing to be considerate of his needs, for example, by turning up the television to disguise what she was up to in her room, when he wanted to sleep.

He was also enraged by his mother's hypocrisy, by the lies she employed to hide the relationship from everyone and to pretend that nothing was going on. She hadn't even introduced Gyuri to her son or acknowledged their affair in any way. Catching the sight of a young man leaving the flat late at night or hearing his mother whispering to someone in the next room, was, however, enough for Gábor to get the picture.

One night Mária made a show of going to bed early and

then smuggled Gyuri into her bedroom under the cover of darkness. Gábor's seething resentment of the situation and of her mother's deceit – on this occasion fuelled by alcohol – provoked him to an irrational and bizarre act. Grabbing the bin from the kitchen, he burst into his mother's room and emptied the rubbish over the sleeping heads of her and her lover.

From this time on the mother-son flat-share took on aspects of a permanent war situation, with neither side giving up an inch of their entrenched position.

The year after Rika's departure Gábor went on a holiday to meet up with his Swedish pen-pal Jörgen. As travel to capitalist, blue-passport-requiring Sweden was not easy or affordable to Gábor, they agreed to get together on the holiday island of Rügen in the GDR.

After jumping through a lot of bureaucratic hoops to get his red passport and buying a train ticket all the way to the Baltic coast, Gábor looked forward to his first foreign trip. That Romanian seaside holiday when he was eight, before his father left didn't count. It was best forgotten.

Jörgen was a laid-back, easy-going, sporty person, not at all intellectual. Gábor realised that he had expected his pen-pal to be like a character in an Ingmar Bergman film, introspective and angst-ridden, despite no evidence of this in his letters. Jörgen had hired a small boat and suggested they sail around the coastline. Gábor, not used to hearty outdoor pursuits, soon caught a cold in the bracing Baltic wind and after a couple of days of practising his spoken Swedish between fits of coughing and sneezing, he said goodbye to Jörgen and took the train to East

Berlin.

He was glad to have bought his return train ticket before setting out from Budapest. Even staying in youth hostels was eating up fast the money he'd brought with him. Eventually he had to resort to sleeping rough in one of the parks.

Wearing most of his clothes, his head pillowed on his canvas rucksack and his jacket as a cover, he bedded down shivering behind a large bush. The rough ground and his hacking cough kept him awake, but he finally fell asleep. The next minute, so it seemed, a torch shining into his eyes and a dog nuzzling his face woke him up. He heard someone shouting, '*Wer sind Sie? Identifizieren Sie sich!*'

His knowledge of German came useful here, even if his excuse of having no money wasn't accepted. After examining his passport, the police patrolling the night streets of East Berlin gave him a choice to avoid being arrested for vagrancy: either book into a hotel or take the first train out.

He returned to Budapest after a only week away and with no desire to go abroad again.

One morning while delivering the post Gábor suddenly felt a sharp pain on the left side of his chest and his breathing became increasingly difficult. He thought he was having a heart attack – though at twenty-two he was far too young for it – and dumping the heavy post-bag on the street he dragged himself to the nearest taxi rank and took himself to A&E.

It turned out he had suffered a spontaneous pneumothorax. It was explained to him that a hole had developed in the tissue of his lung, which made it collapse. The treatment for it involved inserting a tube to suck out the excess air between the lung and the chest wall, in order to allow healing. Gábor found both the condition and the treatment very painful.

After his admission Mária, as next of kin, was informed by the hospital of what had happened to her son. She put in a couple of appearances by his bedside and brought him items necessary for a hospital stay. Gábor suspected that his mother's kindness was only for show and a move meant to disarm him, but he did not have the mental strength to refuse her visits.

He was kept in hospital for a fortnight and was discharged with recommendations to give up smoking and to attend a lung treatment centre for rehabilitating breathing exercises.

When he got back home to Thököly Road he found that his room had been cleaned and tidied up, and discovered that some of his clothes were missing. This made him furious again with his mother and he vented his indignation in a letter to Rika.

'Why can't she respect my privacy? How dare she come into my room and go through my things? I couldn't care less about clothes, but the jumpers you left behind and that pair of needle-cord jeans you sent me were among the ones that disappeared. Could it be that she thought I wouldn't come out of hospital alive, so she had thrown out my clothes? Or could she have given them to that boy?'

Returning to work after his recovery, Gábor were no longer able to cope with the physical demands of delivering the post and was transferred internally within the postal service to supervisory duties. In this position he could observe directly the monitoring and censoring of packages sent from abroad. This solved the mystery of why he never received some of Rika's earlier gifts, books such as Orwell's *Animal Farm*, and prompted him to ask her not to send in future anything even remotely controversial.

But his rebellious nature could not tolerate having a boss or working together with others in an office or spending eight hours of his days on uncongenial tasks. He left the postal service three months later.

As his interests since leaving school had turned overwhelmingly towards languages and by now he had gained a certain command of German, Swedish and English, he thought of trying a bookshop again for his next employment. He could stand it for only a week.

How disagreeable he found that experience was highlighted by his next job, a night guard and doorman in a cemetery. Morbid though this workplace may have appeared to others, it had a lot of advantages for him. He could read and study during his shifts, alone and undisturbed, save for having to open the gate occasionally for a body to be brought into the mortuary.

It was during the cemetery period that he passed his Swedish language exam and started studying Norwegian and Danish, but at the same time he became more and more solitary and lonely. He slept during the day, spoke to hardly anybody at night, and while studying foreign languages he almost forgot to speak Hungarian, at least he hardly dared to utter a word.

Correspondence with Rika was almost his only meaningful human interaction during this time, and she had become his sole confidant, his unique appreciative audience. He wrote long letters to her, six or seven double-sided pages with tiny, backward-slanting writing, essentially substitute journals, with philosophical contemplations, philological ponderings and political musings.

Rika found it hard to excavate the concrete news about her brother from between the lines and even harder to know how to answer. Beyond telling him her comparatively prosaic news – doing a TEFL course, teaching English at various places and her serial attempts and failures at finding a life partner – she did not know how to engage with the non-factual stuff in his letters. While she was still thinking about how to reply, another smoke-saturated letter with challenging intellectual content would arrive from Gábor, who warned that they might lose understanding each other if they don't keep up the correspondence.

His second spontenous pneumothorax, this time on the right side, happened in the following year, on the second day of Christmas. He woke up early in the morning with symptoms familiar to him from the previous attack and called an ambulance from the phone in the hall. The paramedics' arrival and the attendant commotion must have woken his mother up, because the light went on in her room, but she did not come out to see what was going on with her son. Gábor was taken away on a stretcher. After a week's treatment, traumatic as the first time, but its edges rounded off a little by familiarity, he was discharged from the hospital right into the New Year.

The recurrence of his illness led him to read up about its causes and he concluded that he must have had a congenital weakness in his lungs, which was exacerbated by smoking.

This second PTX, as his illness was referred to in the hospital discharge papers, also jolted him into the realisation that co-existence at home with his mother – and Gyuri – had became intolerable. He had to devise a plan to get away from her.

Using his illness as a pretext, he tried to persuade his mother to exchange the flat for two smaller ones, so that they can move apart. 'It would be better for both of us. You would have your own exclusive place and not be inconvenienced by my presence. My coughing would not keep you awake. And I wouldn't be disturbing you when I stay up late at night or when I play music loudly.'

Mária resisted. 'I see no reason for this flat exchange. I'm not dissatisfied with the situation as it is. I don't want any change.'

'But just imagine, you could come to my place for a Sunday lunch, wouldn't that be nice?'

Gábor argued and cajoled, but Mária was still adamant. 'I don't want to move, and that's the end of it. I don't want any more discussions.'

One Saturday morning Gábor came home from work and found Gyuri shaving in the bathroom. Tired after his overnight shift, this face-to-face encounter was like a red rag to a bull for Gábor. Was this boy, this shameless country oaf, going to be around forever? Flaunting his relationship with a woman old enough to be his mother?

'What are you doing here? Get out, I want to use the bathroom.'

'I'm your mother's guest and it's her flat, so you don't tell me what to do...' Gyuri was in no hurry to scrape the shaving foam off his face.

'Aren't you ashamed of yourself? Can't you find somebody of your own age?'

'It's none of your business, it has nothing to do with you. If you had cared about your mother...'

His words having no effect, Gábor tried to drag Gyuri away from the washbasin and shove him out of the bathroom, but he couldn't dislodge the younger and fitter man, who stood his ground. His own weakness enraged him further and using his slight height advantage he suddenly found his hands closing around the throat of his opponent.

Gasping for air Gyuri dropped his plastic razor into the washbasin and frenziedly tried to claw away the strangling hands. Gábor's grip kept slipping, he couldn't exert much pressure, and, as he thought that attempting to throttle somebody who was shaving was not really a very smart idea, his mother rushed into the room and separated them.

Mária's opposition to the exchange and the move subsequently disappeared. It took a few months' search for the right combination of elements to the jigsaw to fit together, but eventually the flat in Thököly Road was exchanged for a one bedroom flat in a high-rise panel-built block for Mária and a room-plus-kitchen flat for Gábor.

14

London Limbo

The letter Rika had received at Hotel Atenea in London two days before her tourist visa expired was from the Home Office. It was an acknowledgement that they had received her appeal. It also contained information about some practical help she could get while the appeal was pending. If she registered for social security assistance, she could receive something to live on while she waited for her case to be heard. This was reassuringly timely as the money she had brought with her was close to running out.

Though she found dealing with the Home Office an uphill battle, she viewed what had happened as nothing less than fair. They made a decision against you, yes, but provided help for you to challenge it legally. They rejected your application, true, but did not want to force you to abandon your intentions by starving you out and making you destitute. She suspected that in many other countries the approach would have been far less humane.

She now had to move out of Hotel Atenea and find cheaper

accommodation. At Miklós & Judit's suggestion Rika, a lapsed Catholic, attended a service at the Hungarian Reformed Church in London with the hope of finding helpful connections among the congregation. In the after-service tea in the vestry, she was immediately targeted by the tenant-seeking missile that was Mrs Polgár, who sussed out what Rika had paid at the hotel and offered her a room in her house in Wembley for just a shade less.

Mrs Polgár had left Hungary with her husband in 1956, and after his death she had been supporting herself by working in a chicken-processing factory and renting out a couple of rooms in her house.

The vacancy in her widow's heart was filled by cats and she offered refuge to all the strays in the neighbourhood. The house smelled of cat pee and in the kitchen there were cat hairs embedded on every greasy surface. Luckily Rika had a two-ring electric plate installed in a cupboard in her room so she could avoid using the kitchen. But the Polish wife of the other Hungarian lodger had no other way of cooking for her husband, and had to negotiate daily the stomach-churning conditions in the kitchen. One afternoon when Rika knocked on Mrs Polgár's bedroom door to hand over the weekly rent, she found her landlady getting up from her bed, fully clothed, with several of her favourite moggies escaping from under the blankets.

To begin with Rika got on well with her landlady. Mrs Polgár had not managed to learn enough English in her twenty years in London, so she was glad of Rika's help in dealing with council officials, meter readers and repair men.

But when Mrs Polgár found out that Rika got her rent paid by 'the social', she became afraid that the Tax Office would learn about her extra income from renting out rooms. 'You've deceived me. You didn't tell me that you're not an ordinary tenant.'

From this time on Rika couldn't do anything right.

'You know, Rika, you have to learn how to clean things properly, to keep your room tidy.'

That's rich, coming from Mrs Stinkyhouse, thought Rika, staying silent.

'Do you need to refill the paraffin heater so frequently?' Rika could have protested that wind was coming through the gaps in her window, but instead she borrowed a coat from Judit and wore it indoors while reading, her legs wrapped in a blanket.

'You're using the electric rings in your room too much, my bill has gone up!' When Rika said she only boiled water for coffee in the morning and heated up a soup in the evening, Mrs Polgár had a ready solution to the mystery: 'You're stealing the electricity through the light bulb. I've heard of such things, my *Freundin* told me.'

But as neither of them could afford to change the situation, they battled on.

Rika's room in Mrs Polgár's house overlooked a school at the end of the cul-de-sac and she often watched the goings on at the gate. It was different from what she'd grown up with in Budapest and she found it fascinating. Parents bringing their children to school and collecting them in the afternoon. The school-day that started later and stretched across lunchtime into mid-afternoon. Girls and boys wearing smart uniforms, but with bare knees and knee socks, even on snowy December days.

On the other end of her street there was a corner shop, run by an Indian family, a be-turbaned man and a woman with a long headscarf behind the counter, This was where she usually bought milk and bread and tinned food. She studied the labels of the unfamiliar products on the shelves, in her daily, unofficial language course. She noticed that the stickers on every item had prices ending in a half-penny.

Across the main road from the Indian shop there was an off-licence, where she sometimes went to for a can of beer. Queueing up to be served she overheard the licencee complaining about the behaviour of football supporters arriving for Saturday matches at the stadium. 'They were jumping over the counter to grab the booze ... I wouldn't call them football fans, I'd call them worse than animals.'

Waiting for her appeal to be heard Rika tried to use the time profitably. She listened to Radio 4 every day to improve her comprehension of the spoken language and bought The Times once a week and systematically went through each article with a dictionary to increase her vocabulary.

For entertainment that did not cost much she would go to Regent's Park, taking the No.18 bus on its long journey to the centre of London. If she could get a seat on the top deck it was also an inexpensive sight-seeing tour. She was puzzled though when the conductor shouted 'All change' as they reached Stonebridge Park.

'Why do we have to get off?' Rika asked the conductor.

'We ain't goin' no furver.'

Rika was none the wiser. 'But the destination on the front

of the bus said Baker Street and I've bought a ticket to go there.'

'Wha'?'

'I want to go to Baker Street. I have a ticket.' Rika was almost in tears. Why can't this man understand her?

'No worries, love. Ah'm goin' to give you a bat'n'wicket and you can change to anovver bus, over there.' The man turned the handle on his ticket machine and handed the emerging paper snake to Rika.

As she stepped off the bus, she heard the conductor's parting words: 'Beau'iful day, inni', love, no need for red'n'yella.'

Rika wondered if they spoke the same language and became seriously worried about her progress in English.

At one of the charities looking after refugees she met a middle-aged lady, Mrs Collins, who personally took Rika under her wing. Initially her help was practical, about how to claim social security or manage unfamiliar everyday life in England. She suggested that Rika should send her letters home via this organisation, to avoid being tracked down at her own address by the Hungarian authorities.

Once able to give a secure return address, Rika wrote to Gábor to say that she had arrived and was safe. She felt she couldn't describe what actually happened with her – the asylum claim and all its ramifications – and couched her letters in vague terms or talked about her observations of English life.

She also wrote to her mother, explaining the reasons for her departure and expressing the hope that her brother would not have to resort to such a drastic move in the future. She learnt from Gábor's next letter that their mother dismissed what she had written as insolent and deserving no reply.

On an early November Saturday she was invited by Mrs Collins for afternoon tea. Rika arrived at the red-brick mansion in West Hampstead bearing a bunch of carnations she'd bought by the tube station. She didn't know what the custom was when someone was invited to tea, and hoped flowers were the right thing to take.

Mrs Collins accepted the flowers and said, 'Oh, you shouldn't have.'

'Have I done something wrong?' Rika was puzzled. 'You don't like flowers?' But she noticed Mrs C – as she mentally referred to her benefactor – put the bouquet in a vase instead of chucking it in the bin.

'No, not at all. I'm sorry, Rika. This is just a polite phrase we use that doesn't actually mean what it seems to mean.'

The misunderstanding cleared up, Mrs Collins ushered Rika into her sitting room, where the low table in front of the sofa was laid with a plate of sandwiches and a shallow-domed, sugar-dusted cake in the middle.

'Do you take milk in your tea or would you like some lemon with it? I don't know what the custom is in your country,' asked Mrs Collins.

'I take milk. I got into the habit when I was on holiday here three years ago. But Hungarians don't usually drink tea, and if they do, they have it with lemon and sugar, or sometimes put rum in it.'

From the doorway of the small kitchen Rika watched Mrs C as she boiled water in a kettle, then poured it into a pretty porcelain teapot that contained loose tea leaves. Rika thought, I'd better not tell her that where I come from people boil the tea leaves in a saucepan, and re-use the same leaves several times, with just a pinch of fresh ones added on each occasion. She reckoned Mrs C would be horrified by such sullying of the English national drink.

Rika loved the experience of the afternoon tea. The soft white triangles of crustless bread enveloping wafer-thin crunchy cucumber slices and the Victoria sponge cake with its raspberry-red heart. She was fascinated by the phrase 'Shall I be mother?', the distinction of 'milk first or milk after', the extra hot water in a jug to top up the pot – why, you could call it an English tea ceremony.

Miklós had some acquaintances who owned a handbag shop. This couple escaped from Hungary in 1956 and as refugees they were given grants to attend universities in the UK – the Western world was feeling guilty for not having helped the revolution. Mr Váradi studied economics at the LSE and his wife became a musician, but after completing their respective degrees they had bought a business and turned shopkeepers. They were always looking for staff and Rika got in touch with them.

The social security benefit Rika had been receiving just about covered her rent and food and she welcomed the chance to earn a little extra money. It wasn't legal, of course – she was not allowed to work while waiting for her appeal to be heard – but as it was cash in hand, nobody needed to know. It would also be better for her state of mind, if she could get out of the four walls of her room, and away from Mrs Polgár's disapproving eyes.

At the shop Mrs Váradi explained that she took a great risk in employing Rika.

'It is dangerous for us, you see, we have a lot to lose. If an official looking person comes into the shop, you have to disappear into the stockroom or pretend you're a customer,' she told Rika.

'And I can't pay you more than £30 a week. But I know you get money from social security, so this should be enough for you.'

Rika had no idea whether the pay was a lot or too little, but was grateful for any help.

She started the following Monday. Her colleagues were a retired English lady who supplemented her pension with part-time work and a young woman, a qualified doctor from Hungary, who wasn't allowed to practice her profession here. They were friendly and helpful, introducing Rika not just to the workings of the shop, but generally to life in England as well. Mrs Váradi popped in briefly a couple of times a week to check on things and then on Saturday afternoons to hand out the weekly wages.

After her first six-day, sixty-hour week in the shop plus a couple of hours of travelling each day, Rika, exhausted, spent the morning of her Sunday off in the launderette and then went for a walk to catch some daylight. The following Sunday she just wanted to stay in bed, but knew she had to go and wash her clothes for the week ahead. Her tiredness was accumulating week after week.

In early December as she struggled in heavy snow through

changes of buses to get to the shop, her thin-soled shoes got thoroughly soaked. Though now she had some money to buy warmer clothes and winter boots, she couldn't because the shops were not open on her day off. As the bad cold she caught lingered on she felt she couldn't stand the experience any longer. She quit the job after a month and a half, just before Christmas, to the great annoyance of Mrs Váradi.

Rika's unhappiness and loneliness over Christmas were slightly relieved by Miklós & Judit's invitation to Christmas Eve and Mrs Collins's to Boxing Day. In the New Year, however, her despondency returned. It was coming up to three months since she had lodged her appeal. Not knowing one way or another was getting her down. How much longer will it take?

She was feeling increasingly cooped up in her room at Mrs Polgár's, as the winter weather closed in and going for head-clearing walks was not sensible. The constant greyness of cloudy skies and the lack of sun for weeks was depressing. She also noticed how changes in the weather affected her: her mood fluctuated and she had frequent headaches whenever the atmospheric pressure dropped. Would she ever get used to the climate in England, she wondered.

Rika's low spirits must have been obvious when she next went to Mrs Collins' office to collect a letter from Gábor, because Mrs C had a suggestion. 'Would you like to see Chartwell? It was the family home of Mr Churchill. We could drive there next Saturday and make a day of it.'

'Yes, I would like that, thank you,' said Rika and thought how kind Mrs C was to take an interest in her and try to cheer her up. And how strange that she still didn't know Mrs C's first name or anything about her, but maybe this was the result of the famous British reserve.

It was good to get out of London, being freed from her room for a day and forgetting her unresolved situation. On the way to Chartwell Mrs C talked about Winston Churchill, who was a personal hero of hers.

Despite being quite an Anglophile, Rika didn't know a lot about him; history was not her strong point. But she loved her first visit to an English country house and especially liked the drawing room with its large windows overlooking the garden, which even in winter looked enticing with its open vistas.

Although Mrs C succeeded in her mood-improving mission, which included another treat of afternoon tea, after the six-hour-long effort to converse in English Rika was so worn out that she fell asleep in the car on the journey back.

15

Becoming an Alien

At the end of March, as Rika was looking forward to the end of the English winter, a letter arrived from the Home Office. It informed her that if she were prepared to withdraw her appeal she would be allowed to stay – as an exception, it was emphasised – for an initial period of a year. She was also given permission to work. She had to register with the Aliens Registration Bureau, report to them every change of work and address, and apply yearly for an extension of her Leave to Remain. Then after four years, all being well, she would be granted permanent residency.

This was it. She had done it. After six months of waiting in limbo, in suspended animation, after almost giving up hope, this came as something of an anti-climax. Just a matter of fact letter. She can stay in the UK.

The news brightened and energised her. She could now start looking for work. But what could she do? It dawned on her that a degree in English language and literature from a Hungarian university was not much use as a qualification here.

She also realised that there was no need whatsoever to smuggle out her university record book. She shouldn't have taken such a risk. Nobody was interested in what subjects her course covered.

Rika had no idea how to go about looking for a job, but Mrs Collins came to her rescue again. She introduced Rika to a Hungarian acquaintance of hers, Mr Pataki, who was working at the National Institute for Economic and Social Research, in the next building to her charity organisation's office.

György Pataki, an émigré of 1956, told Rika that when he joined the NIESR the director suggested to him that it might be a good idea to change his name to something more English-sounding. 'We've had two prominent Hungarians, Lord Kaldor and Lord Balogh, influencing British economic policy during the past decade. It would look better for the Institute if we didn't have another Hungarian economist here.' György didn't mind Anglicising his name and inventing a double barrel surname, so the persona of George Hunter-Pataki was born.

On his advice Rika applied for a vacancy of Statistical Assistant at the Institute. She was formally interviewed by the formidable Secretary and got the job, probably thanks to Pataki's vouching for the quality of maths teaching in Hungarian schools.

The NIESR produced quarterly forecasts for the economy, alternative ones to the Treasury model. Before every publication there were a couple of months of data gathering and number crunching on mechanical calculating devices. Then armed with sheaths of figures Rika had to travel to a house in Gordon Square, where she had to transfer the collated data to punch cards, which were fed into the mainframe computer of the

University of London. The results came out printed on an endless harmonica of green-lined, edge-perforated paper and became the basis of the Institute's forecast. Sometimes, when she made a mistake in the punching of the cards or mixed up their order, the program wouldn't work and she had to try to find out what she had done wrong and remedy it.

Rika was now in a position to move out of her room in Mrs Polgár's smelly cat-shelter of a house in Wembley. On Miklós's recommendation she approached Levente, another Hungarian émigré, who rented out the upper floors of his house in Fulham. She could just about afford what Levente wanted in rent and in exchange she got a furnished room with a kitchen and bathroom on the top floor. Not in great condition – the lino was peeling and the roof sometimes leaked a little – but all for her own use. And the daily tube travel to her job in Westminster was easy.

At the end of the month Rika knocked on Levente's ground floor flat to give him the rent.

'Welcome, Rika, what a rare honour! Come and have a glass of wine with us.'

In the low light Rika could make out the guy living on the floor below her, sitting with their landlord at the table in the bachelor squalor of the kitchen.

Levente lived on his own and encouraged, even expected, his tenants to drop in on him in the evenings. Maybe he thought he had bought their companionship in return for a lowish rent, speculated Rika. When they appeared to be reluctant to socialise with him, he had to catch them when he could, such as rent-payment day.

Levente opened another bottle and poured Rika a glass.

'As I was telling Jani here, we have to be vigilant, there are Communists all around us in disguise. I left Hungary in 1948, after that rigged election. To put it mildly, the Communists were not to my taste, so I thought I'd better leave. But I have never given up the fight against them.'

Rika remembered that many of the people who'd left after the Communist takeover in '48 were sympathetic to the last, fascist, government before the war, so she didn't want to claim common cause with her landlord. Jani didn't seem to pay much attention to Levente's words: he was concentrating on his chain-smoking and on necking as much wine as he could. But Levente was not after a conversation or an exchange of ideas, he just wanted an audience.

Towards the end of the bottle, Levente got onto another of his preoccupations. 'There is this worldwide conspiracy, they control all the banks, world finance, the media, politics, all the governments, everything.'

'Who are you talking about?' asked Rika. After a couple of glasses of wine she wasn't really following Levente's polemics.

'The Jews, of course!' roared Levente. 'Don't you understand anything? Are you shutting your eyes?'

Rika felt uncomfortable hearing Levente's theories, but didn't think she could argue with him. She tried to leave. 'I'll have to get up early tomorrow. Thank you for the wine.'

'Nonsense, sit down, it's still early. Have another glass.'

Later, after another bottle, of which he consumed the lion's part, Levente became maudlin and told them of his latest failure in dating. 'I treated her to a meal at an expensive restaurant and bought her flowers. I even brought her here in a taxi for a nightcap. I thought she would be grateful and impressed by this house. I would've given her the experience of a lifetime. But the silly goose became afraid and didn't stay.'

Finally, as Levente began to slur his words, his reluctant audience saw their chance to slip away. Jani helped their landlord to bed and Rika escaped upstairs, resolving that in future she would put her rent into an envelope and slide it under Levente's door.

Having got permission to stay in the UK and found a job and a place to live, Rika could at last write to Gábor with concrete news about herself, telling her brother exactly what'd been happening to her and giving him her own address, all of which she had been too cautious to do until now.

They also started sending parcels to each other. Rika posted to her brother special selections of English teas, delicacies such as shortbreads and books in Swedish not available in Hungary. Gábor sent his sister copies of his readings that impressed him and the collected works of major poets, trying to ensure that Rika would not forget her Hungarian cultural heritage.

Shortly after Rika had started her job at the NIESR the Queen's Silver Jubilee was celebrated over the two-day Bank Holiday. She wondered through her neighbourhood, where the houses were decorated with bunting and pictures of the monarch, and trestle-tables were set up for the street parties in the roads closed to traffic. Children in Union Jack hats spooned jelly into their mouths and the adults danced on the streets. There were multitiered Jubilee cakes, sing-alongs and Punch and Judy shows.

She observed these sights and happenings with the attitude of someone who wanted to learn the ways of the country she had chosen for her home. She was struck by the affection the Queen was obviously held in and marvelled at the fact that the festivities were organised by the people themselves at local level, and not centrally from above, like the May Day celebrations were in Hungary.

The blustery showers didn't seem to dampen the enthusiasm of the crowds, but after ducking the rain all afternoon Rika went back to her flat, shivering. She wondered when summer was going to arrive. It was now what English people referred to as 'flaming June' and she was still wearing the same kind of clothes, jeans, sweater and jacket, she'd worn when she arrived last October. Was it ever going to be warm enough here that she could wear a light dress and sandals again?

Towards the end of the summer one of Rika's former year-mates at university turned up in London. Although before leaving Hungary she'd confided in nobody else but Gábor, the news about her defection to England apparently got around. Árpád, a not particularly close friend from uni days, was coming for a short language course, and, wanting to check out the rumours, had managed to get Rika's contact details from Gábor.

When Árpád rang her at work he was quick to reassure her that he was not here as 'Kádár's revenge', he didn't want to freeload off her in any way.

Rika didn't invite him to her flat; she was ashamed of its shabbiness and was also afraid that they might run into her quasi-fascist landlord. They had a friendly meal in Chinatown and Árpád extracted from her all the information he was after. Rika wondered if he was planning to follow her example, but he wouldn't say.

Sitting on the tube on her way home Rika mulled over the thoughts and emotions stirred up by her first visitor in England. She recalled certain traditional attitudes among her compatriots towards those who left Hungary.

If the person did well abroad, they would comment scornfully, 'He's only defected for materialistic reasons, in order to make money, to get rich.'

If the person didn't prosper, they gloated, 'Was it worth your while, after all, abandoning your homeland? As you may have discovered, fences aren't made of sausages there either.'

According to these views nothing justified turning your back on the country of your birth, whatever the situation, whatever your reasons.

16

Independence at Last

Gábor was still weak physically after his second bout of PTX, so when it came to the move from the Thököly Road flat to his new place he had to ask a couple of old school friends to help him. He didn't have a lot take, only the contents of his own room and what was left in his father's old workroom. Everything else was claimed and removed by his mother, who was the first to leave the flat in the morning of the three-sided moving day.

As the furniture from Gábor's room, including Rika's old desk, was carried down the stairs by his friends to the small hired van, he chatted to the family who was moving in. They told him that his mother had showed them large bruises on her arm and she claimed it was the result of her son manhandling her and the reason for the flat exchange.

Shocked, Gábor wrote in his next letter: 'I swear to you, Rika, I've never laid a finger on her! I could never have been as drunk as to do that, or to forget it altogether. But what it means is that this boy is knocking our Mother around!'

In the exchange and the move he was so insistent on Gábor in fact did not get a very good deal. His new flat was the equivalent of the kitchen and the adjacent 'maid's room' in the Thököly Road flat.

From the second floor balcony circling the inner courtyard of the building the entry to his flat was via the kitchen, which qualified for its name by having a single cold tap with a bowl underneath. The room – its only saving grace a parquet floor – had a window that overlooked the wraparound balcony and had to be permanently curtained for privacy. There was no bathroom and Gábor had to use the communal toilet, shared by several flats on the same floor.

The condition of these two rooms was so appalling that with the help of his friends Gábor spent weeks scrubbing, scraping and painting before his flat became vaguely habitable. But he was finally independent of his mother, so on the whole he felt it was well worth it.

Even though Gábor's flat wasn't a great prize and he couldn't be accused of having disproportionately profited from the exchange, he felt guilty to have forced his mother into a housing estate flat. How his mother felt about her new place he couldn't have known, since following the move any contact between them had ceased.

He was free at last to have a private life, the obstacles – real or imagined – resulting from sharing a flat with his mother having disappeared. While browsing at a bookshop one Saturday Gábor noticed a young woman, leafing through books at a display next to him. The setting giving him confidence he chatted her up and invited her for a coffee.

Anna had recently escaped from a provincial town and her controlling family, and was just as lonely in Budapest as he was. They started seeing each other and after a few months she moved in with him.

Gábor worked during the night at the cemetery and Anna during the day at her cleaning job. The little time they had together at the flat was spent in reading and studying. Gábor followed his linguistic interests and Anna, influenced by the intellectually dominant Gábor, read out of a desire for self-improvement.

He saw their connection as two damaged people supporting each other emotionally. Anna, a few years younger and far less confident, would have secretly liked a more conventionally romantic relationship, but dared not express her wish openly.

Anna encouraged Gábor to apply to the council for a flat improvement loan, in order to introduce basic amenities to his flat. The plan was to divide the original, so-called kitchen in two, and to create a small internal bathroom with a WC at the back, and a proper kitchen, with a sink unit, a cooker and a fridge, at the front part. In the high ceilinged room they planned to build a self supporting mezzanine floor to serve as a sleeping platform. The interest free loan was to be repaid over ten years and the monthly repayments did not increase the low rent beyond what they could afford from their two modest wages.

His nemesis returned again and again. After his third PTX – a recurrence on his left lung – Gábor packed in his job at the cemetery and joined Anna as a cleaner for a series of organisations, while also doing occasional work as external translator in Swedish for the National Translation Bureau.

Ten months later he suffered his fourth PTX, which was the third on his left side, and when the condition did not respond to the usual suction and drainage treatment in hospital an operation became unavoidable. During a 3-hour-plus surgery via an incision in his back the ruptures in his lung were repaired. The postoperative pain, insufficiently mitigated by medication, felt close to unbearable to him and the chest tubes which drained off fluid from his lung prevented him from sleeping and thus slowed down the healing. He later recalled this operation and hospital stay as the most traumatic period in his life.

On being discharged he was strongly encouraged to give up smoking – though the surgeon admitted that he himself had not succeeded in that – and was told that if he had no recurrence of an attack in five years, his lungs would have recovered to the state of a healthy person.

As he was recuperating from the operation it became clear that he could no longer take on any job that placed even the slightest physical demands on his body. A few months later, not finding anything else suitable, he got a job as an administrator at the National Translation Bureau, where he had been working sporadically as an external translator. The following year he passed his Norwegian language exam, and his status was upgraded to full time translator and editor in Swedish, Danish and Norwegian.

He had finally had a job that suited him and where he could use his linguistic interests and knowledge to make a living. He liked the congenial company of his cultured colleagues – many among them dissident intellectuals who had been imprisoned after the 1956 uprising – and they appreciated his intellectual qualities.

There was, however, a relentless pressure in this job to perform to tight deadlines and to satisfy the demands of the often tearful and occasionally aggressive clients who needed their documents urgently. Gábor found it hard to concentrate on his work in the stressful and noisy atmosphere of the Bureau and routinely took the translations home and worked on them at night before going in the following morning to deliver the assignments. After handing over the finished pieces he and his colleagues usually celebrated their achievements and the sudden release of tension with shots of spirits in the Gödör, the aptly named basement drinking dive, conveniently situated next to the street entrance of the Translation Bureau.

As Gábor at last found a satisfactory occupation, a breach started to open up between him and Anna. She was stuck in low paid drudgery, in jobs giving no intellectual satisfaction, but without contacts, qualifications or specialist knowledge she had no hope of escaping from it. He was under constant and compound stress from the incessant demands of his job and from the fear of not being up to it, of being found out.

Cooped up together in the one-room flat Gábor's inverted living pattern did not help either. He was working at night at the table while Anna slept on the other side of the room and he went to sleep for a couple of hours just as she got up. In the afternoon Anna returned from her job to find him asleep, and he woke up just before her bedtime. When both had been present and awake at the same time in the flat their 'discussions' became intellectually and emotionally devastating quarrels.

It was in this painful and hopeless daily atmosphere that Anna discovered she was pregnant and wanted to keep the baby.

Gábor instinctively recoiled. He realised he had never been wholeheartedly, passionately into their relationship. He saw it as simply the least worst option available when they got together, to comfort both of them, temporarily. Anna, it seemed now, had different expectations. What they had drifted into over time had now become clear and its implications frightened him.

Using practical difficulties as his main argument he first tried to persuade Anna to have an abortion, but gave in to her in the end, because he felt responsible for having allowed the situation to reach this stage, for having led her on.

But the verbal fights over what to do and how they laid bare the real nature of their relationship made Anna depressed, even as her pregnancy advanced.

Gábor came home from work one afternoon and found Anna on the bed, lifeless, next to an empty bottle of sleeping pills. She was rushed to hospital, her stomach was pumped and her life saved. Her suicide attempt was a textbook example of a cry for help, but Gábor used the possibility of harm to their unborn baby's brain to persuade Anna, this time successfully, to have an abortion.

They could not continue to live together after all this. Anna went to stay with a girlfriend and over the following few months gradually moved her possessions out of Gábor's flat. When she came to collect her things they both remembered why they got together originally and how they felt at the beginning, and often ended up in bed together. Gábor resisted Anna's hopeful attempts to rekindle the connection between them. He would have liked to sever the link altogether, but he felt guilty, responsible for Anna's psychological state and, most of all, lonely. So they drifted on, in an ambiguous state as the momentum slowly ran out.

17

First Visit Back

Queueing up at passport control at Budapest airport Rika had the sense that her heart was beating in her throat. A long forgotten feeling of panic and helplessness overtook her at the prospect of facing Hungarian officialdom. Will they notice that her British passport was issued to a Hungarian name? Will they take her aside and investigate? Will this be when her big adventure finally stops?

But when she got to border control window nothing undesirable happened: the official behind the glass had a cursory look at her passport, stamped it and waved her through.

She collected her suitcase from the luggage carousel, wended her way through the nothing-to-declare corridor and emerged from the sliding doors to the waiting crowds in the arrival hall.

Among the people holding up notice boards with the names of individuals they came to collect she immediately spotted Gábor, standing at the side. He looked quite distinct from others around him and not fundamentally changed in ten years, though he was thinner, very pale and had longer, below the shoulder hair.

Rika couldn't risk going back to visit her family before. Even now after having become a naturalised British subject it wasn't entirely safe. She knew that unless she renounced her Hungarian nationality the British government would not be able to offer her protection against prosecution in her native country. Nevertheless, weighing up the pros and cons she bought her plane ticket a month after she received her British passport.

She wrote, separately, to Gábor and her mother and her father, to let them know of her arrival.

Gábor said in his reply that he was going to meet her at the airport.

Her mother wrote back, 'You can't stay with me, I am not alone.' This was a bit baffling to Rika, because she had purposely not asked her mother to put her up, and intended to find a room through the official tourist agency, IBUSZ.

No response came from her father.

As they were leaving the arrival hall Gábor pleaded with his sister, 'Rika, I've been cleaning for a week, please come and stay with me! I have an extra bed, please, don't go to a hotel!'

He also insisted on the extravagant choice, for them, of taking a taxi to his flat rather than going by the multi-legged, airport bus-metro-trolley bus route. After a half-an-hour ride through Pest, which Rika and Gábor spent in manic conversation, the taxi arrived at a building with a battered façade, next to the railway line.

She wheeled her suitcase round the inner balcony of the house to his flat and could sense gossipy glances on her back. 'They'll think I have a new woman moving in with me,' commented Gábor of the neighbours' whispering chorus, as he let her into the flat.

Inside, an army of empty bottles in the corner of the kitchen drew an apology from him. 'Sorry, I haven't had time to return them. Anyway, I regard these as my savings account.'

He proudly showed her the bathroom that was installed behind the kitchen. He had specified the design, and it wasn't decorated in the usual white or blue-green, but in beiges and browns, that he preferred as more tasteful. On the upper half of the very high bathroom walls there were large posters of artistic nudes. Did he put them up after his girlfriend had left? Rika wondered.

In the sparsely furnished room there was indeed an extra bed, which she recognised as her old *rekamié* from the Thököly Road flat. There were some plug sockets and light switches installed three meters high up the walls, revealing the original plans for the construction of the mezzanine sleeping area, that had been put on hold with Anna's departure. The room was in semi-darkness, because the curtains had to be kept drawn for privacy, and stuffy as the window usually needed to be closed to keep out the neighbours' noises, reverberating around the inner courtyard.

Anna had finally moved out of the flat a few months before and Gábor's full attention was now concentrated on his sister, his sympathetic and captive audience. He took time off from work so that they could spend more time together. He wanted to tell her about all he had gone through in the past decade, to show her his writings, to play her his favourite music. Most of these he'd already shared with Rika in letters, parcels and cassettes, but they were no substitute for a face-to-face talk, for the presence of another mind to absorb his thoughts.

On this first visit back, Rika wanted to see her birthplace through the eyes of a visitor, to experience the best face it showed the world. Though Gábor was more inclined to stay in the safety of his flat, he had no choice but to accompany his sister to maximise the time he had with her.

So after breakfast, of fruit, yoghurt and coffee for her and cigarettes, spirits and strong black tea for him, they ventured out from his darkened flat into sunny July.

On these sightseeing outings it soon became obvious that Gábor could not walk fast or far without getting out of breath and had to sit down and rest from time to time. In these pit stops he also needed a restorative double brandy and a couple of fags to keep him going. Having got back to his flat in the afternoons he went to sleep for a couple of hours, according to his usual routine, before another marathon talking session right until the early hours when Rika fell asleep, exhausted and thoroughly saturated in smoke.

Although Gábor was officially on leave, he took Rika along to the Translation Bureau where he worked, to introduce her to friends he made among his colleagues. Gosia, the Polish translator, who had an obvious crush on him; Emil, from Romania, his best friend and drinking companion; and Margit, one of the supervisors at the Bureau and something of a mentor to Gábor. As they went rounds the various offices Rika felt her brother was proudly showing off the sister who managed to defect and make a life for herself in the West. They ended up in the Gödör with Emil, who treated Gábor to the latest office gossip and shots of *pálinka*.

Margit invited Gábor and Rika for a meal at her house in the Buda hills. It turned out he had been a frequent visitor there. They sat in the leafy garden and were joined by Margit's teenage daughters returning from school. The girls clearly liked Gábor, treated him like a cool, laid-back uncle and were totally unconcerned about the nature of their mother's relationship with him.

In the middle of the conversation about books, languages, films and music, Rika had a strange query crossing her mind. Am I sitting in a garden in Budapest talking in Hungarian, or am I in London speaking English? For a split second both scenarios seemed equally possible for her and she could not tell which one was true. This, she thought, was a clear sign that her Hungarian, that was rusty and hesitant on arrival, had become automatic again from a few days' practice, fluent enough to rival English, the everyday language of the past decade in her head.

Getting back to his flat in the evening Gábor filled Rika in on the back story of his connection with Margit. She'd been championing him in the Bureau, weighing in on his side in office politics and preventing entirely unsuitable work dumped on him. Gábor's attitude with unsympathetic colleagues was defensively spiky, which earned him much animosity, and Margit tried to soften the effect of his behaviour. They were also occasional lovers, Gábor confessed, although he did not want to get too involved with her, because Margit's ex-husband and the father of her daughters was still lurking around in the background.

While talking about his love life, present and past, Gábor came out with a jaw-dropping confession. 'By the way, ... you know that I was passionately in love with Éva and we had an on-and-off affair for some time?

'Jesus, what are you saying?'

'You remember when I went to live with father ... that's when it started ... and it continued after I'd moved back to Thököly Road. I was totally infatuated with her ... I even wanted her to divorce father.' He noticed the shock on Rika's face. 'I thought you knew about it.'

'No, I didn't! For fuck's sake, how could I?'

'Well, you were quite friendly with Éva for a while, I thought she might have told you.'

'No, she didn't confide in me, ... not about this. She talked about how much better she found sex with our father than with her previous boyfriends, but she said nothing about you. Honestly, I had no idea!'

Gábor also speculated that one of the children, one of their half-siblings, Viki or Ildikó, might be *his* own child and not their father's.

Rika thought this very unlikely. 'Éva once told me that on their holidays Apu regularly replaced her contraceptive pills with citric acid tablets. She was aware of it and didn't mind.'

Rika understood that their father, knowing Éva's character, was normally relying on the pill to avert the undesirable consequences of his wife's infidelities. By switching her pills – the loving husband bringing them to his wife with the morning coffee – on a month-long holiday when she had no contact with other men, he could ensure the correct paternity of children born in their marriage.

In the light of these and without any evidence, Gábor's suspicion seemed no more than the product of an overheated imagination. Or recollections distorted by alcohol.

Ruminating on past events led Gábor inevitably to the subject of their mother and the rupture between him and her. He had not seen her since they'd moved out of the Thököly Road flat and went their separate ways, five or six years ago now. Though they knew each other's addresses neither contacted the other: she, possibly because in her scheme of life it was the duty of a child to maintain the relationship with the parent; he, because he could not forgive his mother and did not want to see her.

'That woman caused me more harm than anybody else in my life!', he kept repeating. 'I used to think there must've been something wrong with me, that's why she didn't love me. I don't remember any loving act from her, any demonstration of affection or evidence that she loved me! Could I have forgotten it? Rika, was there any? Do you remember?'

Rika had to admit that a loving atmosphere was not what she remembered from their childhood. They had a roof over their heads and food on the table, they had far more than the basic necessities, but not much maternal affection or parental attention. She considered it significant that neither of them had a recollection of their mother playing with them or reading them bedside stories when they were small.

It was all a long time ago, she thought, we should have got over these feelings by now. But she couldn't say this to Gábor, because for him it still seemed a painful, open wound.

She tried to get him to approach it philosophically. 'If we can't remember anything warm or loving coming from our parents, from our mother, does it mean there weren't any? If we didn't feel loved, does it mean we weren't? And if we weren't loved, was it our fault, was it because we were unlovable?'

After a few days of staying with Gábor, Rika felt emotionally wrung out and wanted a respite from the relentless introspection.

She decided to contact her mother, even though meeting her, considering their past rift, did not promise to be easy. The letter Rika wrote to her from London soon after she had arrived there ten years ago and the few postcards she'd sent from foreign places were all one sided attempts at communication, with no responses.

She found her mother's number in the phone directory and called her. Mária suggested meeting up in town and going to Margit Island, which was pleasantly cool in summer.

Both were on time at their meeting place on Blaha Lujza Square and easily spotted the other from afar. They greeted each other with the customary kiss on each cheek. The emotions of a reunion after a decade were betrayed only by a few tears in their eyes, but their words were no more intimate and warm than those between two not-very-close friends.

After taking a tram to the entrance of the island they walked down past the musical fountain, under the shade of oak trees to the rose garden and had ice creams at the open air café beneath striped awnings.

Their conversation was confined to the bare facts of the past years' history.

Rika described her initial dead-end jobs in England, then embarking on a TEFL course, which lead to interesting periods of teaching English in Beijing and Barcelona, and she talked about her intermittent search for life partners.

Mária had less to tell, only about the flat she had moved to and her job, the same she had before at the veterinary institute, which she was going to retire from soon.

They did not talk about the past conflicts between them or about Rika's defection. Mária didn't refer to her estrangement from Gábor and certainly didn't mention Gyuri. Since her mother was not elaborating about her description of 'not being alone', Rika did not feel she could ask without appearing to pry.

As they walked back from the island to the nearest metro station, Mária invited Rika to lunch the next day and, learning that she was staying with Gábor, extended the invitation to him as well.

Gábor had no intention of going. 'I don't want a reconciliation with her,' he said, 'and I don't want to see her. All I want to know is if she's all right.'

So Rika went to see her mother on her own, feeling simultaneously as a spy and a traitor.

Mária lived on the seventh floor of a high-rise block in one of the housing estates of Pest. Dotted among the residential buildings were schools and mini supermarkets, a health centre and a library, children's playgrounds and fenced-in 5-a-side football pitches, all set into tree-shaded, largely neglected parks. Mária's block overlooked a small stream, now all but dried up, and visible on the other bank were small factories and the central heating plant that supplied the estate with hot water and winter warmth.

Inside Mária's south-facing flat the blinds were closed and a large, ineffectual fan was stirring the warm air. In front of the sofa the table was set up for lunch for two people. After the obligatory soup and the celebratory paprika chicken, Mária opened a bottle of red wine and one of sweet Hungarian champagne.

'I remember that you liked the combination,' she said.

Rika had no such recollection, she thought her mother misremembered or made up the memory, but didn't contradict her.

Over the course of the afternoon Mária's tongue was loosened by the wine and she finally came clean about her mystery partner, who was indeed Gyuri. Her initial reluctance to acknowledge him had a lot to do with her experience of people's disapproval of a relationship spanning such a large age gap.

'Most of my friends dropped me after we got together,' said Mária, 'only Rózsi remained supportive.'

'But does he live here with you? Where is he now?'

'I sent him away for a couple of days. Told him to go and visit his mother in his village. I didn't know how *you* would react.'

After Mária had moved into the flat Gyuri was called up for the compulsory two-year military service. When he was allowed out on a few days' leave, the 'home' he returned to was Mária's. Although they had now been living together for several years, his registered home address was still in his village and Mária had not suggested that he should change the official registration to her flat. She had also evaded his repeated marriage proposals, saying, 'We are all right as we are, why change something that's working.'

Rika's reaction to her mother's relationship with Gyuri must have looked sufficiently non-judgemental in Mária's eyes to finally risk introducing them. Rika suggested meeting for dinner at a small restaurant on Thököly Road, the scene of family celebrations during her growing up, and a place which during the summer months served food in its well shaded garden.

Both Mária and Gyuri dressed up for the occasion, which made Rika realise that going out to a restaurant was a special event for them and they wanted to present their best image.

Mária, her hair freshly tinted and permed, wore a light grey *kosztüm* with a white pussy-bow blouse and discreet gold jewellery. Twenty-seven year old Gyuri was dressed in a pale beige summer suit and white open neck shirt, which revealed a gold medallion glinting in his chest hair.

Seeing his fresh-faced, blue-eyed, blond-moustachioed handsomeness Rika could see how her mother fell for him. But the contrast of youth with plump middle-age was striking. She thought an uninformed observer could view their trio as Rika and Gyuri the young couple and Mária the mother-in-law.

When it came to ordering Gyuri immediately assumed the role of the man in charge and revised the women's choices with what he judged more appropriate. A dislike of *pálinka* was waved away, a simpler dish was replaced by a more elaborate one, a melon arrived crowned with unwanted whipped cream, and wine was pressed on them beyond wishes or capacity.

The conversation did not flow easily and there were long awkward silences, which Rika tried to fill by asking Gyuri about himself. He described his free-roaming, rural childhood in the village near the Tisza river, where his mother still kept chickens and fattened a pig for slaughtering every winter.

Recounting their shared history Mária and Gyuri talked about their memorable holidays: in Pula at the beginning of their relationship, when Mária went skinny dipping for the first time in her life, or recently in Malta, the souvenirs from which they were wearing around their necks. Gyuri told the story of Mária making him a beer-cake – twenty bottles of beer arranged in a circular pattern on the carpet – for his birthday during his military service. And he proudly mentioned Mária's last birthday present to him: a precious ticket for the upcoming Queens concert in the Népstadion in a week's time.

Towards the end of the meal the atmosphere at the table became relaxed, as Gyuri felt accepted and Mária reassured. Rika went to the toilet in a mellow mood, only to find on her return that Gyuri had surreptitiously asked for the bill and paid it.

She was silently fuming. *I* invited them to dinner, so why did *he* pay for it behind my back? I know they don't have a lot of money. Sure, Hungarians always fight over who will pay the bill, but this is ridiculous! It's treating me like a stranger. Or trying to show who's in control.

She expressed her annoyance aloud and did not accept Gyuri's defence that she was now a guest in Hungary. With this cloud over the mood of the evening they said good-bye outside the restaurant.

'I hope it won't be another ten years before we see each other again,' said Mária.

It had not been easy tracking down the whereabouts of her father's family. When she went to their current address in Kőbánya nobody answered the bell at the gate, no car was parked in the yard and the house appeared to be locked up.

She then rang her father's workplace and learnt that he was on his month-long annual leave in his holiday chalet in the Börzsöny hills. There was no telephone there and no way of contacting him before she had to go back to London. Luckily a colleague of her father's had some idea where the place was, so the next day she took the train from the Western Railway Station to the Danube bend.

Rika got off the train at the small station – no more than a raised platform with a sign – and following the jotted down instructions headed towards the blue-green hills.

As she was walking along the narrow, curving road from the station, she felt the strength of the mid morning sun on her neck. She'd forgotten how hot the summers could be in Hungary. But it was still more bearable than the same temperature in London before she had left. Maybe because of the difference in humidity, she thought.

After a few minutes she came up to a small bridge spanning a stream, with a fork in the road beyond. A few children were playing along the bank and because the directions in her notes were fairly vague, she thought it would be better to ask them.

'Do you know the Varga family? Do you know where their house is?'

She was not prepared for the explosive answer.

'We are the Vargas!,' shouted in unison two teenagers, a boy and a girl, echoed by a younger girl, who was petting a beautiful Irish setter.

'Well, if you are the Vargas, then I am your sister, Rika, from England.'

No wonder Rika did not recognise them. Andris was four and Viki three when she left, and Ildikó wasn't born until the following year.

Leading the way, the children ran ahead skipping and jumping, and burst through the gate shouting to their father, who was repairing something on the veranda, 'Apu, Apu, Rika is here! Rika is here!'

'Rika? Which Rika? Your mother's friend?' asked their father in a don't-bother-me tone, then shouted to his wife through the kitchen window, 'Éva, your precious friend has turned up!'

'No, Apu, no, it's Rika from England!'

Tamás wiped his hands on a rug and went to welcome his eldest daughter. 'I thought you would be fat by now,' was his initial reaction, before going on, 'Why didn't you tell me at the time that you wanted to leave the country? I could've helped.'

Over lunch there was mutual catching up on the news of the intervening years, with much questioning of Rika by her siblings, boasting of her children's achievements by Éva, and loss of interest disguised by jovial platitudes on Tamás's part.

The children were very excited by their newly discovered sister and proudly wore their just acquired London Underground t-shirts. They took Rika on an excursion in the neighbourhood, to the little creek at the bottom of their long garden and the small woods beyond.

Rika was delighted to get to know her siblings. She observed how the characters of the two eldest ones, already glimpsed in the toddlers ten years before, had developed into their current selves: Andris, his mother's first-born and favourite, clever and self-confident; Viki, an overshadowed second child, equally intelligent, but shyly unconfident. And the unknown youngest, Ildikó, the pet of both of her parents, who was mad about animals and inseparable from their dog, Aliz.

In the evening there was *szalonnasütés*, an indispensable event to every summer holiday. Tamás and Andris built a camp fire in the garden and brought back from the woods long sticks, onto which Éva and Rika speared alternating thick slices of fatty bacon and onions.

As they were preparing the spits in the kitchen Éva told Rika stories of how in the early years when they went out as a family Tamás was often mistaken for the children's grandfather. But she added, 'When we got together everybody said it wouldn't last; but now we've been married for sixteen years, longer than your father was married to either of his previous wives.'

The *szalonnasütés* was a great success. The delicious drippings were caught on large slices of country bread and pickled cucumbers completed the simple feast. As the embers died down, the evening cooled and darkness fell, they moved indoors, continuing the conversation late into the night, the adults sipping beer and the children Coca Cola.

Rika then joined Andris, Viki and Ildikó, climbing up to the attic of the chalet. Before going to sleep she taught them how to count to ten in Spanish and Chinese, which their young brains soaked up without fail.

The next morning she had to go back to Budapest. Her father and the children saw her off. 'Let's keep in touch from now on' suggested her father and her siblings promised that they will write to her. As the train was pulling away from the little station she heard Ildikó practicing the Chinese numbers she'd just learnt: *yi, er, san, si, wu, liu* ....

Rika and Gábor spent the last day before her return flight to London with shopping for presents and treats unobtainable in England. In one of the upmarket interior design shops she bought, despite his protestations, a hand-crafted, leather framed mirror, for his beige and brown bathroom.

In the afternoon after getting back from town, Gábor had his usual couple of hours of sleep. From the curtain-shielded, open window came the sounds of children fighting in the courtyard and neighbours returning from work, the smells of cooking and the increasing cacophony of dozens of televisions. When he woke up, he lit a cigarette, took a swig from the bottle next to his bed and called his sister over.

Rika was finishing her packing, trying to fit towel-wrapped bottles and vacuum-packed sausages into her suitcase. She stopped, went across the room and sat down on the edge of his bed. They were both conscious that these were the last few hours of her visit and felt the sadness of the coming separation.

Gábor sat up in bed, put his cigarette out in a saucer on the floor and pulled his sister towards him.

Rika thought he wanted to give her a hug, but his mouth was aiming straight at hers.

Her heart started beating madly. What the hell ... what does he want? raced through her mind.

Then realisation struck. It was unmistakeable. She became scared. What can I do? How can I get out of this fix, ... without wounding him with my rejection?

At the same moment doubts came. What if I have misunderstood his move?

Instinctively, she drew back from him and in a voice choked by agitation she stammered, 'Gábor, ... I don't ... I don't think ... I don't think it is a good idea.'

Then, without waiting for his reaction she stood up and went back to the other side of the room and, not knowing what else to do, continued her packing.

After a long silence Gábor said, jokily: 'You are right, Rika, perhaps it's better that you don't go back to England carrying an extra little present, hidden inside you.'

18

A Momentous Year

'Szia Rika, it's the 5th of March, Saturday. I've managed to coax this dinosaur of a tape recorder back to life. I don't feel like working at the moment. I've just come back from the shop where I spent my last 300 forints, so there's no money left for going down to the *kocsma* for a drink. But at least I don't owe anything now, not to the bank, not for the rent or for the gas or electricity bills. There's no sword of Damocles above my head, like a couple of months ago, when disconnection threatened because I was behind with the payment.

You could say I'm not very good with money. It's true, I don't budget or save, what comes in I spend straight away. Perhaps it shows the absence of a woman in the household. But other people also have money problems and my income is quite low.

That's why I recently started taking on 'express service' works, in which the translation has to be done straight, on sight, sometimes while the client waits. It's stressful, doing fifty pages in eight hours, roughly the output of three or four people. It earns the translator about 40% of the hefty premium that the Translation Bureau charges to the client.

Arrangements like this are the result of introductions of more market elements into what has effectively become a mixed economy here. But private work is also getting more scarce; people have very little money. A client may have paid a 1000 forint deposit for a translation and then doesn't come to collect it, because he can't find the balance of 2000. This shows how poor people have become. And an apt illustration of how the economy is stalling.

The atmosphere here is getting highly politicised. With inflation running at about 50%, people are getting more embittered and desperate. To prevent strikes or civil unrest they had to be given something, so we now have *glasnost*. And the resulting situation is irreversible. As someone's put it, the toothpaste cannot be squeezed back into the tube. Mind-blowing, unheard-of, earthquake-like changes have been discussed recently, Rika. Like the introduction of a multi-party system and walking out of the Warsaw Pact.

By the way, I want to send you this cassette before the 15th of March, because God knows what will happen then. This is the first time it's been made a national holiday. Everybody will be out on the streets. I'll go too. You have to be there. If there are enough demonstrators, they won't be able to disperse the crowds with brutal force.

Also, the situation's become critical because these idiots, this stupid regime, built on forty years of counter-selection, didn't have the intelligence to realise that this would be an important occasion, that this date has a special significance and to come to some kind of agreement with the opposition, somehow, in any form, and to take over the organising of the event themselves.

Sorry, Rika, I'll shut up now about politics. I have had enough of it, to tell you the truth, but unfortunately one is compelled to take a stand every day, to form an opinion, because in Hungary in the present day you cannot live an intelligent life without taking part in politics.'

*

During the spring of 1989 there was a string of strikes on London Transport and one fell on the date of Rika's interview. After a lot of try-ons she put together, from her wardrobe of customised charity shop finds, a relatively smart outfit that she could walk in. Fortunately, it was not raining and the forty-minute walk in the sunshine from her flat to Bush House among the crowd of commuters didn't feel like hardship. She was used to walking, anyway, as exercise or to save on fares.

Lately her English teaching jobs had been mostly part-time and short term, and searching for some additional or permanent employment she applied for a job at the Hungarian Section of the BBC World service. To her surprise she was invited for an interview.

'How did you get here?' was the first question of the friendly young woman, the deputy head of the Section. Rika did not realise that this was small talk to relax the interviewee, one Londoner asking another about her way of coping with the strikes. She replied with a potted history of her escape from

Hungary and her life since, before realising what the interviewer had meant and became embarrassed. After a brief chat, Rika had to translate several news passages into Hungarian and do a sound recording test to determine whether she had the right voice for broadcasting.

She was called in a week later for her first shift as a Production Assistant, on probation, to work from early afternoons towards the evening news broadcasts that went out to Hungary. As the news items came in from the agencies or from the BBC's own correspondents she had to translate the ones assigned to her by the editor and type up the Hungarian versions on old clanking typewriters. A colleague showed her how to record her translated pieces on the big reel-to-reel machines and how to edit out the mistakes, hesitations and uhms by splicing the tape together. Then the finished tapes, together with the scripts marked with their exact duration in minutes and seconds, were sent down to the studio to the producer.

Initially Rika found none of it easy. She had rarely spoken or read Hungarian for many years now, she was fumbling for words and had to consult the dictionary frequently. The translations took her a long time and felt laboured and awkwardly phrased. Her colleagues, some of them refugees after the failed 1956 revolution, helped her selflessly with editing and revision, which she accepted gratefully. With practice her fluency and speed improved, and, instead of sending down a pre-recorded version, she was allowed to read out her translations live in the studio.

Performing on air was nerve-racking. When she was one of the two newsreaders on the programme, the persistent fear at the back of her mind was that she would have to translate some last-minute news directly on air. Then one night that was exactly what happened. Just as they were about to go live the editor rushed into the studio with a printout of breaking news. Seeing Rika go white as a sheet her experienced colleague promptly took over from her and read out the simultaneously translated news item, seamlessly and professionally. That night Rika found it even harder to get to sleep, the usual adrenaline rush after her late evening shifts even slower to ebb away.

The difficulties of the job were more than compensated for by the exciting news from all parts of the world. As the pro-democracy student protests started in Beijing, somebody recalled from her CV that Rika had spent some time there. From this point on she was considered the unofficial Chinese expert of the Section, despite her protestations that she had no more privileged access to information than any reader of British newspapers. She was interviewed for her comments and invited to a live Saturday discussion about the events in China. On these stressful occasions she felt like an impostor and was subsequently ashamed of her performances.

After Gorbachev's visit to Beijing Rika was asked in an interview what she thought the outcome of the pro-democracy protests would be, whether an eventual military suppression was likely. Not having the wisdom of an experienced journalist who would never give an unequivocal prediction, she said the events in Beijing were so advanced, so peaceful, so widely reported in the western media, that she did not think the regime would dare bring the troops in against the protesters. She added that according to the Chinese tradition rebellion by the people was a sign that the mandate of Heaven had been withdrawn from the rulers. The young, self-assured interviewer, who doubted whether the Chinese Communist regime would pay heed to this traditional view, later duly reminded Rika of her foolish prediction.

Broadcasting the news about Hungary – developments that nobody had thought would ever happen – made Rika feel as if somehow she was a witness to history being made. The mass demonstrations on 15th of March, which forced the regime to begin negotiations with the emerging opposition. The dismantling of the electrified fence on the border with Austria. The moves to exonerate former Prime Minister Imre Nagy.

Some of these changes she had already heard about from Gábor. It now struck her as truly bizarre that programmes about events occurring in Hungary should be broadcast from London aimed at a Hungarian audience. In the past when news in the local media were lies and propaganda it made sense for people to tune in to foreign broadcasts to learn what was *really* happening in their own country. But those times were hopefully over now, she thought.

*

GÁBOR: Szia Rika, it's the afternoon of the 24th of May and I am here at father's place. I've brought my tape recorder to make a sound picture for you. I didn't want to record them without their knowledge, so just asked everybody to say a few words to you. But it's difficult to get them speak. Ah, here comes father, on a break from his current DIY project. Apu, please come and say something to Rika.

TAMÁS: Well, Marika is far away. (*To Gábor*) Your hand is shaking ... Rika, szia, I don't know what to say to you. I haven't seen you for ages and I'd really like to see you. You don't write very often. I don't write either, it's true, but, you know, that's life. Now, excuse me, I'm right in the middle of something ... I have to get back to it.

GÁBOR: (*To the children*) If you gather round, I'll put the microphone down here in the middle and you can all talk to Rika.

ILDIKÓ: (*In a loud voice at breakneck speed*) Szia Rika, I have a cat, Felix, he was a street-cat, has a swollen foot and he often throws up. (*Andris sniggers in the background*) What shall I say? At school we had a Russian competition and I flunked it. On Friday we're going on a school trip. I no longer do karate, I got fed up with it. I have a parrot, called Lóri, who cannot speak ... ha, ha, ha. I had fourteen fish in a tank as well, but all except two died, ... my other animals include a tortoise ... and Andris and Viki. (*Clapping and laughter in the background*)

ANDRIS: (*Confidently*) You know, Rika, I am about to go in for an English language exam, at middle level and then later for the higher one. It will be useful when I apply for university next year and for jobs afterwards. I don't want to be a doctor any more, I've changed my mind. I'm going to study computing. I find that much more interesting.

GÁBOR: (*Encouragingly*) Viki, come a bit closer to microphone and talk to Rika.

VIKI: (*In a small, timid voice*) Szia Rika, ... I'd like to thank you for the French newspapers you've sent me. They were very useful, I managed to read quite a few articles in them.

GÁBOR: Do you know any French poems by heart? Can you recite your favourite?

VIKI: I like Apollinaire's *L'Adieu*. But I don't want to recite it.

GÁBOR: Why not? Rika would like to hear it.

VIKI: Yes, ... but I don't want to recite it.

(*A clang, like the sound of a large piece of metal falling, can be heard*)

GÁBOR: Andris, shouldn't we go out and help Apu again?

ANDRIS: No, he said that we should wait until ...

GÁBOR: Rika, while we've been talking here, outside father is trying to turn 90 degrees the metal staircase that leads upstairs from the yard. It weighs about 300 kilos and it's moved with Stone Age methods, painfully slowly, millimetres by millimetres. It's now three quarters done, but Apu doesn't know how he will finish it. He'll work it out eventually, he says. Andris and I have been helping him, but we've got bored with waiting around.

(*The sound of a car and a dog's barking can be heard. Andris goes out to the yard to open the gate for his mother. Ildikó goes to the kitchen to help*)

GÁBOR: Well, Rika, this is all I could squeeze out of the family so far. I have a good mind to erase what father's said, his usual empty joviality, because what's the point?

VIKI: No, Gabi, you don't understand, Apu can't express his feelings.

GÁBOR: But *why* can't he express them?

VIKI: Why do you have to put everything into words? ... You and Rika don't really know Apu very well.

GÁBOR: This is an opportunity to keep in touch with his first-born child, ... and he ignores it. I don't know, if I were in this situation, I would grab the chance ... to tell her how I am, what's going on here. For fuck's sake!

VIKI: You're so afraid of each other, ... and so distant from each other ....

GÁBOR: You mean we are afraid of hurting or offending each other?

VIKI: No, not that, ... you don't know each other ... you're so fundamentally different.

GÁBOR: That's undeniable.

VIKI: I think, a lot of things ... don't have to be put into words ... they can't be ... you have to feel them ... and one feels more than what can be expressed in words.

GÁBOR: But words are wonderful ... and if you don't have words for something, if you can't verbalise it, you understand it much less.

(*The tape recorder is switched off, then back on later*)

TAMÁS: (*Coming into the living room*) I'm dead tired now.

GÁBOR: In the end, Rika, with the help of a neighbour, who provided more muscle power than all of us put together, we finally moved that blasted staircase into position.

It's unbelievable ... such self-confidence ... that without any previous idea how, father would start lifting a fucking iron staircase so heavy it could've killed any of us if it had slipped ... this supreme self-belief, I really admire in my father.

(*Sound of the TV in the background*)

Well, Rika, now the TV is switched on and the family is taking bets on the result of the AC Milan vs Steaua Bucharest match, with everybody wishing the defeat of the Romanians, not just in this household but in the whole country as well.

(*The tape recorder is switched off and then back on later*)

GÁBOR: Rika, the football's over, it was a great match and the Romanians were thoroughly thrashed.

Now they're starting a regular late night TV program, *At the Close of the Day*, and I'll just let the tape run, for the few minutes left.

PRESENTER: Our discussion tonight will cover a topic that is very much in the air. In the last few weeks there have been a lot of talk in the media about the trial of Imre Nagy, about the legality of his execution and the necessity for his rehabilitation.

In the light of recently discovered documents, an article in the paper *Hungarian Nation* questioned whether rehabilitation is the correct term to use, because rehabilitation implies culpability, which is not applicable in his case.

I invite the writer of this piece, one of our guests tonight, to analyse the ramifications of this question.

GUEST: Yes, examining the documents it became obvious that the trial and the sentences went against the Criminal Code at the time, in other words they were unlawful. Now, laws may be broken by criminals, but they can also be broken by administrations of justice. The court that tried and sentenced Imre Nagy did not act *lege artis*, did not apply the law correctly.

Therefore, the task of the administration of justice today is not the rehabilitation of Imre Nagy, but rather the rehabilitation of the jurisdiction, of the law itself.

PRESENTER: If we look at the White Book, which recorded the wording of the sentences handed down, right in the first paragraph we find several absurdities. Let me read out these few lines … (*The tape runs out*)

'Szia Rika, I'm recording this the day after I went to father's. During the football match they, unwisely, put half a bottle of French cognac next to me and I duly finished it. I left about eleven and went out to the main road hoping to catch a taxi but none was coming.

Waiting at the bus stop there was a homeless-looking man and, feeling friendly and talkative under the influence of the cognac, I started chatting to him. The man, in his forties, apparently recently released from prison, for what offence he didn't say and I didn't ask, told me at length about his disastrous first marriage and was still unburdening himself when we got off at the last bus stop. He wanted me to go for a beer with him, but I was keen to get home.

Just then four young lads turned up, shouting to the homeless guy: 'Now we'll get even, you dirty scum bag!' They knocked him out with a single blow.

I tried to reason with them, 'Leave him be, can't you see what a pitiful state he's in already!'

This turned the lads' anger onto me and I got a couple of flying kicks to the kidneys and punches to my face and chest. These simply floored me, I couldn't do anything, just lay there, but still conscious. The boys then administered a few further kicks to my arms and legs for good measure, before leaving the scene, their thirst for a fight satisfied, shouting back, 'That's what you get for fucking my little sister!'

By this time the homeless guy had disappeared. I struggled to get upright and dragged myself to the taxi rank across the square. At home, every part of me hurting, I made an inventory: black eye and purple-black cheek bone, spitting and vomiting blood, chest and kidney pains, and arms lacerated in the attempt to shield myself and the tape recorder.

Nothing broken – only the cover of the tape recorder, ha ha ha – and the internal bleeding will heal in time. The damage to my masculine self-esteem may take longer. This incident shocked me by revealing how defenceless I am. I should have fought back, I should have been able to defend myself, even if they outnumbered me. If I had been less drunk, Rika, this wouldn't have happened, because I could've run away in time. On the other hand, if I had managed to run away, I would now rebuke myself for being a coward.

After a few hours of painful sleep, this morning I went down to the phone box on the corner and rang work to tell them I wouldn't be in. A client was due to come in to collect a translation I'd promised for today, but I didn't want to have to explain in the office about the black eye ... clearly not the result of falling down some stairs. In the heat of the phone box I was close to fainting and almost dropped the receiver, my arm was hurting so much.

I asked to be put through to Margit, who promised to smooth the matter over with the client and, on learning what had happened, wanted to visit me after work. She was very concerned about me. It seems she really loves me. But I told her, thank you very much, I really appreciate your kindness and I knew you would offer to come over. But if you do, I may not open the door to you.

Rika, this is all. I've not filled the whole tape, but I want to send it to you quickly. And I'm waiting for your reaction.'

*

During the summer Rika was called in for an increased number of shifts at the World Service as the regular staff went on holidays, so she was often there to broadcast the extraordinary news right after they broke.

Solidarity winning an overwhelming victory in Poland, leading to the peaceful fall of Communism.

The funeral of Imre Nagy on Heroes' Square in Budapest, which drew a crowd of a hundred thousand and a sharp speech by Viktor Orbán, a young democrat, who demanded free elections and the withdrawal of Soviet troops.

The Pan-European Picnic, which opened up the Austrian-Hungarian border and allowed East Germans to escape to West Germany.

In the middle of September Rika was sent on a two-week in-house Production Assistant course, to officially learn how to do the things she had been doing for months. Fully trained, she resumed her shifts at the Hungarian Section, and the unbelievable, exhilarating news continued to pour in.

There were daily reports of mass protests and demonstrations demanding changes in East German cities, such as Leipzig.

In October Communist rule in Hungary finally ended after forty years and a Republic was proclaimed, on the anniversary of the 1956 revolution.

She still hadn't replied to Gábor's last tapes. When they arrived she had listened to them straight away, but it was not easy to react to them or find the time for a re-listen and the lengthy, well-considered response he expected. She always felt that her replies were inadequate and the worry that they were not intellectually interesting to him inhibited her. And now on top of her English teachings and the BBC shifts, she had got a part-time job at the British Library and started a new relationship, which consumed most of her free time. So the tapes continued to sit on top of her chest of drawers, gathering dust accusingly.

*

On the 9th of November Gábor left the Translation Bureau in the early afternoon. Feeling tired he decided to put off going to pay the electricity bill till next week. At home he had something to eat, hit the bottle and fell into a dead sleep. This was the only way he managed to get to sleep at all these days.

He woke up after nine as the noises in the house were subsiding. It was now too late to do some chores, cleaning or washing clothes, even if he had wanted to, without disturbing his neighbours. That was the problem with his life style. He lived during the night, this was the daily schedule that evolved to best suit his needs. But it didn't fit into how society worked, nothing was open during the night, so he couldn't run errands, go shopping or to see a film.

Usually he would start working about ten and continue until dawn, but today he did not feel like settling down to a difficult Flemish translation – weren't they all getting like that recently?

He turned on the radio searching for a foreign news broadcast about the continuing political ferment in East Germany and was just in time for the late news from London. After the familiar signature tune of the trumpet solo came the slightly crackly announcement in Hungarian, 'This is the BBC World Service. Here is the news read by Varga Mária.'

Hearing his sister's name he would really have fallen off his seat, had he not been sitting on the mattress on the floor. He knew that Rika was working at the BBC, she had written to him about it in the spring, but he had no idea what her job actually was. In the semi-darkness of his room, under the circle of light cast by the lamp on the bookshelf, he heard her voice from thousands of kilometres away and felt she was talking to him directly.

But the news emerging from her reading were even more astonishing than the fact she was reading them.

In Berlin the East German leadership tried to calm the escalating protests by announcing at a press conference: 'Private travel abroad would be allowed without prerequisites.'

A surprised journalist asked, 'When would these take effect?'

The government spokesman, shuffling his papers but not finding the answer in them, improvised and said that, as far as he was aware, it was effective immediately.

After watching this on West German television, East Germans flocked in huge numbers to the checkpoint in Berlin. The border guards, having received no orders, decided to open the gate. Thousands flowed through, celebrating and crying. More gates were forced open, people climbed over the Wall at the Brandenburg Gate and many were chipping away at the structure with hammers and pickaxes.

Overnight, the actual barrier and the symbol of division in Europe crumbled and fell.

*

Rika's shifts at the Hungarian Section were usually arranged a few days earlier by a phone call from the programme's editor. A week before Christmas, however, the call came from the recently appointed head of the Section, who replaced the much-loved veteran journalist and poet, an émigré of 1956. The new boss introduced himself and asked Rika if she could come in for several shifts during the following week.

As he was speaking Rika remembered a colleague's remark that the Section preferred using casual staff during public holidays when the salaried, permanent staff would have had to be paid double rates. She declined the invitation, explaining politely that she wanted to spend Christmas with her family. The new boss was surprised by her unwillingness to sacrifice her holiday and, hinting at the uncertainty of her future at the BBC, rang off.

Rika and Anthony, her boyfriend of three months, celebrated on Christmas Eve with the traditional Hungarian fare of wine soup, fried fish and walnut *bejgli* and the next day in English style with turkey and all the trimmings and Christmas pudding. Replete with the big meal, they switched on the TV in the evening, looking for a film to watch, and stumbled on the late news.

The first item taken from Romanian television showed the capture of the Ceauşescus, the footage of their hasty trial and their execution by firing squad. A gruesome end to the year of revolutions.

19

All Change

'Should we have our wedding in Budapest or in London?' asked Anthony. They were sitting on the top deck of the No.19 bus going through Islington, when he started talking of marriage.

Rika was surprised. They had known each other for barely six months. This seemed far too soon to her. And academic too, since Anthony was married, she had learnt. His American wife spent long stretches of time back with her family in Connecticut and he conducted his relationship with Rika in the space of his wife's intermittent absences. But he was going to get a divorce, as soon as he could, he promised.

He was very keen to meet Rika's family. 'Write to your father and ask if he could introduce me to some investment opportunities in Hungary. For a fee, obviously.' Anthony continued, 'Tell him I'm a millionaire.'

They arrived in Budapest a couple of days before the first post-communist parliamentary elections, in which parties other than the previously ruling Socialist Workers Party could participate.

They were met at the airport by Tamás, who drove them straight to their hotel in the centre of Budapest. It became immediately clear to Rika that she would have to interpret everything between them – Tamás's English was not quite up to conversational level and Anthony spoke no German, very little Spanish and of course no Hungarian.

Anthony lost no time in unfolding his proposition to Tamás. He explained that he was a director of a Project Development company and was scouting for business ventures to develop in soon-to-be-opened-up Hungary. When such a project came off, the person who acted as the intermediary would get a finder's fee – a certain percentage of the eventual investment.

Tamás was very excited by the prospect of making some serious money. He had retired three years earlier and his state pension – and there was no other kind – was a sorry fraction of his previously respectable salary. He still had a few casual private jobs to supplement his income but also three teenagers living at home and a younger wife accustomed to a higher standard of living.

Sitting in the hotel lobby, Tamás told them that he had already identified some business possibilities among his contacts and was ready to fix up meetings for next Monday.

'Look, how keen your father is!' said Anthony to Rika.

Tamás sheepishly explained his eagerness: 'I need the money, I have three children'.

'No, Tamás, you have five children', replied Anthony, 'have you forgotten?'

'Yes, yes, of course ... I mean I still have three to support.'

Rika felt embarrassed. Is Anthony trying to ingratiate himself with me, she thought, by scoring points against my father?

The first round of the elections took place on the following Sunday. Tamás had volunteered to help the Alliance of Free Democrats with their IT system on that day, so he invited Rika and Anthony for lunch at his house on Saturday.

The purpose of the meal seemed to be to impress Anthony with lavish hospitality. Partly to welcome the exotic, foreign boyfriend into the family, but mostly to entertain a hopefully lucrative business contact for her father, suspected Rika.

Éva prepared famous Hungarian dishes and presented them as she imagined they would be in an upmarket restaurant. The best china and crystal glasses came out of the cupboard and you could hardly see the damask tablecloth from the myriad dishes on the table.

The wine flowed, but the conversation, in English for the guest's sake, was halting at first. Viki studied French and Ildikó did German at school, and Éva spoke no foreign languages, so Rika and Andris had to interpret for all the others and everything was said twice, in mirroring languages.

Andris was about to turn eighteen, soon to finish his studies at the *gimnázium* and start a University course in the autumn. On the basis of his knowledge of English he quickly built a rapport with Anthony and their exchanges monopolised the conversation around the lunch table. He asked a lot of questions about Western businesses, realising that here was a valuable source of information about what the future would be like in Hungary, now that the communist/socialist economic model was, as everyone thought, on the way out.

Tamas felt his son was taking over the talk at the table and was overshadowing the cultivation of his own business connection. He tried to butt in and offer suggestions but was at a language disadvantage.

Andris pointedly ignored his father's advice and asked Anthony instead. 'I want to work for a Western organisation when I graduate. Can you tell me how to go about it?'

Anthony relished the experience of being regarded as a business mentor. He suggested that Andris should find internships with Western companies when they set up operations in Hungary and promised to send him books on economics and business management.

The first round of the elections did not produce a conclusive result, so a second round, a fortnight later, became necessary. In the meantime, with no more immediate work for the Free Democrats required, Tamás could accompany Anthony and Rika on the initial meetings of the business introductions he had set up.

In the next few days they went to a small computer firm, a once renowned, but now old-fashioned café and patisserie, and a textile factory in dire need of modernisation.

Tamás acted as the driver and a link between the local ventures and a would-be foreign investor.

Anthony behaved like a saviour coming to the rescue of antiquated and run-down Hungarian businesses with superior Western business acumen and finance.

Rika was the interpreter and translator at these meetings – a set-up she felt was unsatisfactory because of her rusty Hungarian and her ignorance of the special technical terms in these various fields. She was puzzled, how had she ended up with this role?

In the brief gaps between these business engagements Rika took Anthony to meet her brother. Gábor was happy as usual to see his sister and glad that she had found a partner, but there was also some jealousy creeping into his reactions. He felt a little supplanted in her affections and tried to assert the special sister-brother connection between them, but was thwarted by having to use a language that was not his best. His fluency in spoken English was far below the level of his reading competence and he became visibly frustrated when he couldn't express the teeming ideas in his head as quickly as they came or when he couldn't grasp the nuances in Anthony's words.

Rika empathised with her brother, but didn't know how to make the meetings more comfortable for him. Anthony, in a friendly gesture, gave Gábor a giant bottle of Unicum as a meeting present and Rika wondered if he was trying bribe her brother to like him.

Introducing Anthony to her mother was a different kind and magnitude of awkward. During the conversation over another guest-impressing lunch Rika had to translate every single word uttered in both English and Hungarian. Her head was shuttling between opposite sides of the table and her mind between languages, back and forth, until she became thoroughly confused.

This resulted in some truly comical moments when Anthony would say something and Rika would turn to her mother and translate his words for her from English into ... a differently worded English.

'Say it in Hungaaariaaan!' chanted Gyuri when Rika made this mistake for the fourth time.

Does he think I do it on purpose? thought Rika. Or is he irritated because he doesn't understand English?

Anthony mentioned to them his business intentions in Hungary and Mária, wanting to help, suggested some practical ways of finding relevant information, nothing more complicated than looking thing up at the Yellow Pages.

Gyuri, tanked up on home-brewed *pálinka*, was annoyed that he hadn't thought of these, and immediately snapped his wife down, 'What do you know about things like that? What do you know at all?'

Rika did not like his scornful tone and waded in. 'Don't talk to my mother like this!'

Gyuri exploded, 'Who are you to talk? You, who neglected your mother for ten years?'

Taken aback by this attack, Rika tried to defend herself, 'You don't know the history, you don't know what happened ... it's not like that ... it's not ...' she stammered.

'You left and didn't care whether she lived or died. Where were you? Gallivanting abroad. And who did you think looked after her all that time?'

Anthony could not understand a single word of the argument swirling around him, but picked up on the animosity from the tones and the body language. After hearing Rika's summary of what was said, he said to Gyuri: 'Do you want us to leave?'

Rika duly translated it.

'No, no, of course not' – Mária was attempting to diffuse the situation – 'he didn't mean it like that.' And trying to mollify him, she added: 'Gyurikám, please bring another bottle from the fridge and let's have a toast.'.

But Gyuri stormed out of the room and seconds later they heard the flat's front door slamming.

'Don't worry about him. He will come back when he's cooled down.' Mária gave the impression of speaking from experience.

But Gyuri hadn't returned by the time Rika and Anthony left half an hour later, and the tone of future encounters were set.

The result of the first free elections was that the previously ruling Hungarian Socialist Workers Party lost power and the recently formed Hungarian Democratic Forum, in coalition with two smaller parties, formed a government. As had been expected, the country was opened up to foreign investment.

In the course of the following year Rika and Anthony went to Hungary several times in connection with his business negotiations. Rika felt, and knew that she was, not fully competent in the role of translator/interpreter and wandered why Anthony didn't engage a trained professional for these meetings. She was beginning to suspect that for Anthony going on foreign business trips provided acceptable excuses to be away from his wife. He could spend time with Rika on business expenses, and get her, even if imperfect, knowledge of the local language into the bargain for nothing.

After the initial enthusiasm on both sides in these talks, Anthony's projects hit bumps along the road. To Rika's eyes the main problem seemed to be a clash of expectations. The Western side looked for control of these, in their view, worthless businesses for very little money; the Hungarian enterprises wanted lavish compensations for allowing access to their markets. As the moments of committing investment funds drew near, Anthony got cold feet and the negotiations petered out one by one.

The following Christmas Rika went to Budapest to spend the festive season with her family. As she came through the double doors into the arrivals hall of the airport, her father was waiting.

'Where's Anthony? Hasn't he come with you this time?', asked Tamás.

'We've split up, it's a long story,' replied Rika and on the drive to his house she told her father the edited history of the past few month.

After the possibility of the Hungarian business ventures evaporated, Rika's relationship with Anthony had changed. Contact between them had dwindled to a couple of phone calls a week, a dim sum lunch in Soho on Saturdays and on rare occasions sex in her flat. He was still married, afraid that his wife would claim half his wealth if he had made moves to leave her.

With increasing frequency Rika was thinking of putting an end to this intolerable set-up. This is hardly a relationship, she kept telling herself, he hasn't introduced me to his mother or sister, or any of his friends, and I'm held at the margins of his life, like a mistress.

Then Anthony's wife moved back to the States and filed for divorce. He was free at last to commit to Rika, but now he never mentioned his previous plan of getting married. Not that Rika was that keen on marriage, but it irked her that he had forgotten his proposal.

Pleading lack of money, Anthony was reluctant even to get a place together with Rika. After his wife's departure he wanted to move into Rika's small, rented flat, and offered to pay only the slight increase in the utility bills his presence would cause. It didn't occur to him to suggest splitting all the expenses for the flat he wished her to share with him. It's really mean of him, reckoned Rika, especially as he professes to be wealthy and I'm always on the verge of having to claim Income Support.

This was the last straw for her. After an agonising night she wrote to him at his sister's address. She expressed her unhappiness and frustration with how things stood between them. 'I feel unvalued and like a dirty secret in your life. We don't even meet for long enough to talk.' She said she couldn't continue as before and wanted to end their relationship, unless there was some change. 'If you think there is a future for us, maybe we could talk about working towards it.' She thought he would reply to her letter, she hoped he would try to change her mind, but didn't hear from him again.

'I've never liked Anthony, there was something about him that didn't feel right,' said Tamás, when Rika had finished her account. 'He struck me as very insecure. You're better off without him.'

Rika didn't recall her father saying any of this before, but maybe a parent can only express misgivings about a child's choice of a partner after a break up. 'I'm sorry you were caught up in his schemes,' she said, 'you've put a lot of effort into it and got no introduction fee in the end.'

'Well, that money would certainly have come useful. But it looks like he hoodwinked everybody. I don't believe he was a millionaire. He was such a cheapskate.'

Soon after Rika and her father had got back from the airport, Éva arrived home from work and they all sat down to a meal together. Of Rika's siblings only Ildikó was there, Andris apparently out with his girlfriend, and Viki, her father said, was staying late at her classes at the university.

As the afternoon turned into evening and Viki still didn't appear, Tamás finally came clean. When his wife left the room he said to Rika in an undertone, 'Viki has moved out. She had a lot of conflicts with her mother and went to live with her boyfriend's family. It'd be better not to say anything about it to Éva. And you can sleep in Viki's room.'

The next afternoon Rika went to see Viki, who told her everything their father didn't. The clashes between Viki and her mother had started while she was still at school. Under the guise of 'education' Éva routinely slapped her daughter for disobedience, for talking back or not behaving as she thought she should. After Viki had started medical school, her blossoming intelligence and youthful attractiveness was proving even more intolerable to her mother, who was now in her forties and fast losing her looks.

'Then I discovered that Anyu had been unfaithful and I told Apu,' confessed Viki. 'Maybe I shouldn't have, maybe it was really naive of me, but I love him and I thought he should know. Then there was a big row and Anyu hit me – nothing new in that – and kicked me out. And Apu didn't stand up for me. He said afterwards that it was for the sake of family harmony.

So I had nowhere to go and when I couldn't get a place in a hall of residence, the parents of Balázs said, come and stay here, there's plenty of room in this big old flat. They have been so kind to me, treating me as if I was their own daughter.'

'Nobody talks about your absence at home,' said Rika. 'It's an unmentionable subject. Apu only told me in the end because he couldn't explain why you didn't return by the evening.'

'Yes, I know,' said Viki, 'everybody's afraid of Anyu. Except Andris, her favourite. But I speak with Ildi regularly, and Apu secretly comes over from time to time and gives me a little pocket money.'

In her subsequent visits to Budapest Rika stayed at her father's place, and from this base went to see her brother, on most days, and her mother, as few a times as she could manage.

Gábor felt he had got his sister's attention back, just like he had before Anthony had arrived on the scene. But because of their more limited time together now, the intensity of the first visit wasn't repeated. Rika didn't mind that at all; she was glad she had somewhere to escape from the endless, alcohol-fuelled, emotional soul searching and reminiscing with her brother.

Having observed the hold alcohol had on him, Rika tried to think of ways of removing Gábor, even if only temporarily, from the environment that contributed to his addiction. Several times she invited him to visit her. 'I'll send you a plane ticket and you can stay with me. We can go and see all the famous places in London and in England.'

Gábor always fended off his sister's offers. 'It's very generous of you, but I can't accept it. ... I don't want to be a charity case.'

Later, a friend of Rika's came up with a plan to enable Gábor to leave Hungary. Marion – a colleague at a previous job – had became something of a mother substitute. Rika's urgent phone calls to Marion for help always resulted in an invite for tea and cakes, accompanied by excellent, if unconventional, advice.

When Rika returned from Budapest once again distressed by seeing her brother's decline, Marion said that she would be willing to enter into a marriage of convenience with Gábor. Even by her free-thinking standards it sounded a strange solution.

'Don't you think the thirty-year age difference might make it suspicious, might make the immigration authorities suspect it's not a real marriage, it's a sham?' Rika asked.

'That would just show how narrow-minded people are. Your family has a penchant for relationships with big age gaps, anyway. We just have to do our homework and present our case the right way. This could be the saving of your brother.'

Rika thought Marion's proposition wildly eccentric and unlikely to succeed, but put it to Gábor all the same. He declined it. 'I'll solve my own problems. I don't need an old lady's help.'

While staying at her father's place in Kőbánya Rika was well placed to observe the family dynamics at close hand.

Andris, now a few years into his university course, was supremely self-confident. He was always boasting about how much money he was going to make and scoring imaginary points against his sister, who had to work hard on her medical degree course. 'I told Viki, you'll have to study ten times as much as me, but I'll earn ten times as much as you'.

He was constantly challenging his father, which reminded Rika of a young lion intent on assuming the old one's leadership. But it wasn't simply one generation replacing another. The fundamental change from a socialist to a market economy had just begun when Andris started university. He was learning the ways of operating in the new economic system. But for Tamas, who worked and retired in the old regime, the change came too late.

After his official retirement Tamás's sphere of activities became mostly confined to the house, except going out for food shopping or paying bills or on his occasional private assignments. Éva, who had recently landed an office job with the police, went out to work every day and earned the greater proportion of the household income.

As Éva had become the main breadwinner and the traditional roles were reversed, the power balance in the family shifted. She didn't feel she had to justify her absences from home, to explain sudden after-hour 'work meetings' or to account for events she 'had to attend'. The resulting blazing rows between their parents lead Andris to spend more time with his girlfriend and Ildikó, still at school, to hide in her room.

Over one uncomfortable Christmas period Rika saw – and wished she hadn't – many signs of their deteriorating marriage.

On one occasion Éva was telling Rika about something that happened to her at work. It was a trivial story, with bragging refrains of 'I told the boys repeatedly not to do it that way and I was proved right.'

Rika, having stopped listening early on, reacted in a way that obviously didn't satisfy Éva, who proceeded to re-tell her story, as if she'd wanted to hammer her meaning home, as if she couldn't stand the silence. Her self-hypnotising voice droned on and on.

When Éva finally went out to get herself cigarettes, Rika heard her father, reading on the other side of the room, commenting under his breath, 'How she lies! And what a dimwit!'

On another evening watching the film *Divorce Italian Style* on television with Marcello Mastroianni as the male lead, Éva kept needling her husband, 'You see, Tamás, here is a real man!' and taunting him with the age difference, 'Look how young and virile he is.'

A few days later it was the New Years Eve party at Éva's workplace and she insisted on going alone, without Tamás. 'Civilians are not invited,' she said, 'so no husbands or wives will be there.'

Tamás didn't believe her. 'Don't try to pull the wool over my eyes, sweetheart. What are you hiding?'

'I'm not hiding anything, but *you* are *not* coming. No more discussions.'

Éva marched upstairs to prepare for going out. In the course of the afternoon she had a bath, depilated her body, manicured her nails and blow-dried her hair, before spending over an hour in front of her dressing table, painting herself a new face, sustained by cigarettes and glasses of wine. As she came down to the sitting room in her sparkly tight-fitting dress and defiantly ordered herself a taxi, she remarked to Rika, 'You know, your father's been getting very jealous lately.'

The next day Éva came home at midday and refused to explain where she went after the party. She ended the ensuing quarrel by threatening Tamás. 'If you don't stop hassling me, I'll bring home my service revolver and let you have a couple of shots!'

Returning to London after witnessing these scenes Rika resolved to stay away for a while from that upsetting battle ground. She continued to keep in touch with Gábor, whose letters and tapes became once again her source of information about the happenings in the family.

Next summer Ildikó finished secondary school and Gábor was asked by Éva to the graduation ceremony. He turned down the invitation, saying he didn't like official occasions, and promised instead to go to see them a few days later.

At his father's house Gábor found everything in a state of change. Ildikó didn't get into her choice of university – the vet school had a notoriously difficult entrance exam – so she was going to take some time out from studying, get a job in the meantime and try again next year. She was in the middle of her packing to go off for summer volunteering at an archaeological dig.

Andris had just graduated from his university course and, following a final-year internship, landed a job at a Western company, as project manager on their electronic brokerage and trading services in Budapest. Getting a position with a foreign firm was considered a major coup. Éva couldn't stop boasting about her brilliant son and of the great future that lay ahead of him. She was less happy that his western-level salary enabled him to rent an upmarket flat of his own in Central Budapest, and her favourite child moved out of the family home as soon as he could.

Tamás was also proud of his son's achievements but wanted to take some credit for his son's success. 'I taught him all that he knows about computers, without me he wouldn't have got to where he's now,' he commented to Gábor.

Andris had installed specialist software on his father's computer at home, so he could follow the rise and fall of his few Telecom shares on the Budapest stock exchange. This made Tamás feel as if he was still part of his son's world, still not entirely relegated to the economic scrapheap of retirement.

He was less emotional than his wife about their son moving out, 'He has his own life to live, he cannot be expected to hang around here forever.'

'You just don't care about him,' was Éva's reaction, which triggered another slanging match between them.

As the insults between his father and Éva were shooting back and forth in front of Gábor, he excused himself by pleading a lot of overdue work and beat a hasty retreat from the house in Kőbánya.

A few months later Gábor heard from Ildikó that her mother had moved out of family home. He relayed this news to Rika, hoping she would resume her visits to Budapest.

20

Endgame

On that memorable Saturday Rika was at home, making a curtain for her bedroom, while simultaneously watching television. She was not a royalist, she hadn't gone to inspect the sea of flower tributes at Kensington Palace or to keep vigil in front of Westminster Abbey. Nevertheless she wanted to witness this unprecedented event – the funeral of the ex-wife of the heir to the throne, after she had been killed in a crash following a car-chase by paparazzi.

Her attention was at first divided between measuring, cutting, pinning and stitching the fabric, and catching a glance now and then at the procession of the gun carriage with the coffin and the young princes walking slowly behind it. But after the ceremony had started and she heard Elton John's song and Earl Spencer's tribute to his sister, Rika couldn't continue her work for the tears blurring her eyes. The music and the words throat-chokingly rekindled her own grief, the still raw memories of less then three months ago.

Viki was the one who rang Rika in London with the news. From the start of her medical course she'd fallen into the habit of visiting Gábor in the afternoons as the gaps in her university schedule allowed. She would turn up on the spur of the moment and knock on his door, never knowing whether he would be at home or willing to open his door. If she was admitted they would have heart-to-heart conversations: she would confide in him and he would put a philosophical gloss on the situation, like a sympathetic mentor to a sensitive protégé.

She had a lot to get off her chest over the years. The intensifying clashes with her mother, which culminated in getting kicked out of the family home and finding shelter with her boyfriend's family. The subsequent break-down of her parents' marriage, her mother's moving out and her own return to live with her father and Ildikó.

When on the latest occasion there had been no reply to her knocks, Viki was not alarmed. She knew that Gábor was at home, light appeared to be filtering through the drawn curtains, but she did not try to see if the door was locked. Perhaps there was somebody else inside with him, she thought, a woman maybe, that's why he didn't answer. She pushed a note under the door and went home.

Two days later Viki's boyfriend Balázs came over in the afternoon after his long shift as a paramedic. He was uncharacteristically silent and kept looking at Viki searchingly. 'Don't you know what'd happened?' he asked finally.

He had heard colleagues at the ambulance station talking about a case they were called out to and the name of the patient was mentioned. 'Isn't that the surname of your girlfriend?

Could it be a relative?' one of them asked.

'Yes, but it's not an uncommon name. What's the address?'

It turned out that a neighbour, noticing Gábor's front door ajar, went in to investigate. He had found Gábor lying in bed, with the bedside light on, an open book and a plate with a dried-up sandwich in front of him. He looked as if he had fallen asleep while reading, but even from a distance it was plain that he was not just asleep. It was also obvious that somebody else had been there before; there were empty spaces on the shelves where the television and the hi-fi must have been. An ambulance was called. The paramedics arrived quickly, but it was already too late, all they could do was to pronounce the death, call the police and have the body taken away for an autopsy.

The official cause of death was myocardial infarction. As Viki explained in laymen's terms, Gábor's long-term heavy drinking weakened his heart muscles, which ultimately led to heart failure.

For years Rika had been haunted by the thought that her brother was in essence committing suicide, slowly, with alcohol as his chosen instrument. While during the PTX years he may have flirted with alcohol for its anaesthetising effect, his steady involvement with it started after finding his near-ideal occupation at the Translation Bureau. There a shot of *pálinka*, vodka or brandy became a lubricator of mental cogs, a reward for a difficult translation completed, a dissolver of stress or a celebration of camaraderie.

After Gábor had become the Bureau's in-house specialist in

Swedish, his evident talent and accomplishments lead to him being asked to translate documents from other languages, such as Faroese or Icelandic as well. He saw no problem dealing with these linguistically related languages if given sufficient time. He enjoyed the intellectual challenge.

But as he completed more tasks originally not in his job description, he was given more work outside his competence, sometimes bizarrely so.

'You mean you don't know Finnish? Why, isn't that also a Scandinavian language? ... Not from the same language family? I'm sure you can do it by tomorrow!'

'Here's a piece in Dutch, it's needed next week, you can learn it by then'.

He sweated blood working overnight or through weekends with little sleep and a lot of alcohol to complete the assignments. But the pleasure and satisfaction he once had from his work was gone, it all became unrealistic expectations and unreasonable burdens piled on him without limit.

Gábor was intelligent enough to recognise the damage alcohol was doing to him and in the early years tried to give it up periodically. Seeing Rika on her visits to Budapest he sought her reassurance that she could detect no lessening of his mental faculties. His great fear was that alcohol was destroying his braincells and his sharpness of thinking would decline. There was the 'control specimen' of his sister in front of his eyes, who from a similar start had *not* wound up in the same predicament.

Yet he would not seek professional help and stated confidently – or conceitedly? – that he could deal with giving up drinking by himself.

His earliest stabs at what he termed abstinence relied on the prop of beer, which Hungarian men regarded as not much more than a soft drink. He avoided the pitfalls of celebrations at work and with minor deviations he stayed on his version of sobriety until an unguarded moment took him back again to the hamster-wheel of hard spirits.

He had made several serious attempts at drying out. In a tape-letter to Rika he mentioned not having had a drink for a record nine months. He came across as clear and coherent, his mind sharp, his analysis of the current political situation perceptive and articulate. It gave Rika hope that he had managed to turn things round.

He told her how much he was saving every day by not drinking and as the result was able to buy a word-processor for doing his work at home. With insight into his own psyche he thought it was lucky he hadn't got into other habit-forming substances, because with his addictive personality he wouldn't have been able to handle them. But he still questioned whether giving up drinking was altogether worth it. Without this artificial animating and brightening agent his life became immeasurably greyer and more boring.

Witnessing a few more of Gábor's attempts at giving up and the crises getting ever deeper, his friend Margit eventually persuaded him to go voluntarily for a detox. She organised his hospital stay and looked after him throughout the process.

Initially Gábor was treated in intensive care, with medication and vitamins, under heavy sedation. When the DT and the withdrawal symptoms had subsided he was transferred to a psychiatric unit. There he surprised the psychiatrist with his self-awareness and a frank acknowledgement that he *was* an alcoholic, in contrast to the usual delusional denial by such patients.

Then, during one of the doctors' daily visits he overheard a whispered discussion about giving him the alcohol withdrawal drug, Antaethyl. This frightened and scared him – he dreaded losing his autonomy and becoming totally powerless when faced with the medical world. So after the following week-end's home leave he did not return to the hospital, not even for weekly check-ups, and effectively discharged himself.

He maintained that this time there was no danger of his backsliding. 'I've seen the fragility and instability of our human consciousness,' he told Rika, 'I've gone right through and approached the point where the balance of the mind is destroyed and cannot be restored again. And that's why I cannot allow myself to have even a single drink. Because after the first shot I may be able to stop, but the next time I might not, and then in a month I would be back where I'd been before.'

Back to work after his detox Gábor was given – and had to accept – difficult or near-impossible assignments. Translations not from, but into, German or Dutch, or an indecipherable handwritten Flemish character reference or a birth certificate from Romanian to Swedish for a would-be refugee. 'Gábor will do it in his current situation', reckoned his colleagues in the Translation Bureau, 'he needs the money, he needs this job.'

Gábor felt his life had become enveloped by a cloud of deep

sadness, he felt completely excluded from the pleasures of social interactions by his abstinence. His colleagues hadn't grasped the change in his situation and continued to behave towards 'dry Gábor' as they behaved towards 'drinking Gábor'.

'It's Kasia's birthday today, come over to her office after the last client, we'll toast her,' a colleague would ask, before realising, too late, 'Oh, of course you can't!'

Gábor, feeling ashamed, would invent excuses and decline invitations. After a while he would no longer be asked and with this his already small circle of social connections contracted further.

His absolute abstinence lasted about a year. When he eventually fell off the wagon, he did it so spectacularly that he lost his job.

Due to the need for an autopsy there was a long wait before the death certificate could be issued, the body released to the family and the funeral organised. Rika looked for the earliest affordable Malév flight from London to Budapest. She spent the intervening days re-reading the huge pile of Gábor's letters and listening again to his tapes from the last few years. Her days ended with uncontrollable crying fits that brought her uneasy sleep and blocked sinuses by the following morning.

She remembered the last time she saw him, during the previous year. The by now regular visits to Budapest had called for a carefully balanced split of her time. As usual, she stayed at her father's, because he had a spare room, squeezed in a few duty visits to her mother and went to see Gábor almost every day.

After basking in sisterly attention for two weeks, on the last afternoon Gábor tried to delay Rika's departure. 'Let me read you something ... have you heard this recording of Jan Garbarek? ... here is a Swedish writer I came across ... just listen to this fantastic piece of Turkish folk music I found ... please stay a little longer,' he pleaded with her again and again.

Rika was going to take their father and siblings out for a meal, and asked Gábor to come too, but he did not want to.

To put off the moment of their parting he walked with her to the bus stop, talking non-stop, cramming more confessions into the last few minutes. When the bus came, they said goodbye, 'till next year', 'write about all this soon', 'no, send a tape' and she got on board.

The articulated vehicle turned onto the overpass and Rika caught sight of her brother's thin, stooped, long-haired figure, lighting a cigarette and walking slowly, ever so slowly, like an old man, away from the bus stop back to his flat. She felt guilty for leaving him like that. I'll put things right, I'll make it up to him the next time I come, she thought.

As it turned out there was no next time.

Ahead of Rika's arrival in Budapest Tamás started organising the necessary arrangements. He contacted Mária and suggested they meet up at a square nearby and go on from there to his house to discuss the sad matter of their son's funeral.

They had not seen each other for twenty-five years. 'You will recognise me by the Reuters baseball cap I'll be wearing,' he half-jokingly told her on the phone.

There was no need for an identifying sign, Mária thought

when they met, he didn't look drastically different from his former self, except having become stouter or lost more hair. The purpose of the cap may have been to hide his baldness or to indicate his keeping up with current trends by wearing it backwards. He gallantly told Mária that she hadn't changed at all these years.

Arriving at his house they found Ildikó, his youngest daughter, washing the windows, which she gladly interrupted to make coffee for them. Stepping up to be in charge, Tamás proposed that himself and Rika would take care of the necessary official business and all the expenses related to the funeral, to which Mária, revealing her long standing estrangement from their son, willingly consented.

The day after Rika had arrived in Budapest she went to the Translation Bureau to talk to Gábor's colleagues. She couldn't find Margit who was on annual leave, but an older colleague, Csaba, a Swedish expert who admired Gábor's achievements in their shared field, volunteered to give the eulogy at the funeral.

Gábor's best, and perhaps only, friend, Emil, invited Rika for a drink at the *Gödör*, referring to it as Office No. 9. Sitting at the dimly-lit booth in the basement, he ordered two shots of brandy, drank one himself and poured the other one out onto the floor, as a libation in memory of his dead friend.

He talked about how Gábor helped him, a refugee in Hungary, after the Romanian revolution of 1989. His eyes glinting with the liquid sheen Rika had seen in her brother's – the eyes of an alcoholic – he recounted Gábor's last few chaotic months at the Bureau. A bust-up with colleagues, resignation, re-instatement, a spectacular fuck-up with a client, dismissal, re-instatement, Emil didn't quite remember in what order. And the last week, when he went to see Gábor in his flat, and found his door locked.

As Gábor was not religious and a Catholic priest conducting his funeral was out of the question, Rika and her father wanted to hold their own farewell ceremony, with remembrances accompanied by some of Gábor's favourite music. The graveside as a setting for this being unsuitable – no means of playing music – they thought of having it at the mortuary at the cemetery before the coffin was taken to the graveside.

The officials at the mortuary at first did not want to accommodate their unusual request. They thought the place was not suitable, they thought the family should hire a hall somewhere else to hold a memorial service, maybe later, after the funeral had taken place. They relented, however, once they were offered money for their help.

The day before the funeral Rika and her father went to the cemetery for last minute checks on the arrangements. They took the mixed tape, prepared by Rika and Viki with excerpts of music, and handed it over to the attendants with detailed instructions about the timings to allow for the spoken contributions in between.

Just as Rika and Tamás were about to leave the cemetery it occurred to one of the mortuary officials that somebody who knew the deceased should check if they had got the right body, to avoid a mistake before the coffin was nailed down. Somebody had to go in to the cold storage area and identify the body, dead for almost three weeks.

Tamás blanched and shook his head, he couldn't even say he couldn't do it.

Having been left no choice, Rika had to do it. She took a deep breath and followed the official in, her eyes fixed on his feet, as if glued to. She noticed his heels were worn down at the outside edges and caked with mud. She moved like an automaton, without looking left or right. When the shoes in front of her stopped, she looked up, had a quick glance, gave her confirmation and rushed out.

No matter how brief the glimpse was, the vision of that darkened face, like an Egyptian mummy's, continued to linger in her mind and threatened to become etched on her retina. She later consciously tried to erase the image to stop it reprinting itself on her brain. Every time it surfaced from her memory she attempted to transform it, mentally dissolving it into a happy photo of her brother from several years before.

The mourners gathered in the bare, utilitarian room at the mortuary where the coffin, propped up on a bier and surrounded by wreaths, was waiting to be taken to the graveside.

There were not many people there. Gábor's parents, plus Gyuri, jealously glued to Mária. His siblings, including Andris, who was dressed in all black, like a gangster from the nineteen-twenties. A handful of Gábor's colleagues, including Margit and Emil. One neighbour of Gábor's and one of Mária's. A large, bearded figure lurking on the edge of the congregation, not making contact with anyone – Laci, his cousin.

Tamás had contacted his estranged brother with the news of his godson's death, but Pál excused himself by pleading arthritis and difficulty of walking.

Among the wreaths, at a prominent place in front, Tamás spotted one sent by Éva and he angrily shoved it to the back, trying to hide it behind others, while muttering something under his breath.

In his eulogy Csaba painted a picture of how Gábor's secure childhood world was destroyed by his parents' divorce. How he craved affection, yet fearing disappointment he repelled friendly approaches by his behaviour. How he wanted to live his life on his own eccentric, non-conformist terms, as a lone wolf, if need be. How his unconventional talent was overwhelmed by the misunderstanding and lack of empathy of others. How he barely managed to keep his head above water, until he could do it no more and finally let go.

He ended his oration with a quote from one of Gábor's poems – *You're alone on the streets / behind the curtains / the lights are turned off* – before offering his personal credo. 'Forgive us, Gábor, for not enlightening you about the meaning of our human existence, for not letting you into the secret that the solution to our loneliness can only be found in a higher dimension, in the boundless love of the One who willed us into being and who is waiting for us offering eternal happiness.'

Rika was taken aback for a moment by this unexpected insertion of religion into their remembrance of Gábor and regretted not having discussed with Csaba the tone of his speech. But it was her turn to speak next so she couldn't dwell on the thought for long.

She had always intended to say something valedictory at her brother's funeral, but until dawn on the actual day she did not know what or whether she could deliver it without breaking down. She lay in bed sleepless, agonising over her speech. As it got light outside finally some words surfaced in her mind. *Gábor, if your spirit is still fluttering here among us, we would like to give you our solemn promise, that we will always remember you, we will never forget you.* She jotted them down half-consciously, without a second thought, without asking herself if she really believed, as these words suggested, in the existence of the soul or an after-life.

Hours later, having got to the cemetery in a daze and then been fairly undone by Csaba's emotive tribute, she struggled to utter her few words, before predictably dissolving in tears. Then Dido's lament, one of Gábor's favourite pieces of music, soared up in the room to end the informal ceremony. *Remember me, remember me, but ah, forget my fate.*

As the last notes of the music were fading out, it suddenly occurred to Rika that her own, not very original little speech had inadvertently given the answer to the universal plea of the departed.

The coffin and the wreaths were loaded onto a motorized cart and the mourners filed out of the mortuary following it. Walking at the front of the small congregation was Rika, each of her arms linked by a parent, while on Mária's other side Gyuri was clutching his wife's arm, supporting or perhaps guarding her.

At the graveside, in the absence of officiation by a priest

and as a final farewell, Viki read aloud Kosztolányi's much loved poem 'Funeral Oration'. The lines of the second verse – *Profit all of you by his example / This is what man is like, a singular sample / No copy existed before, nor does one at present / As on a living branch each leaf is different* – brought forth contagious tears and sobs all round, and Viki struggled to finish her delivery.

Then the coffin was lowered unceremoniously into the grave, flowers were thrown on top, followed by handfuls of earth. The gravediggers hung around, pretending to be busy, until Tamás handed out some money to them. The mourners lingered for a while by the grave, condolences were offered again and promises of keeping in touch were made. Mária invited her daughter to lunch the day after.

Before the people finally dispersed from the graveside someone, unconnected with the family, remarked that the rain had held off and the weather stayed nice for Gábor.

Back at Tamás's house he and his daughters held their own private wake: reminiscing about Gábor and drowning their grief in wine. Viki and Rika each recalled memorable moments from their own, different, relationships with their brother. Ildikó, though not having known Gábor as well or had the same emotional bond with him as her sisters, kept them company out of sympathy, disappearing into the kitchen from time to time and coming back with plates of food to soak up the wine. Even normally impassive Tamás lamented the loss of his first born son. Csaba's eulogy seemed to have pricked his conscience about abandoning his first family and the chain reaction it unleashed for Gábor.

In the run-up to the funeral Rika had been too overwhelmed by Gábor death and the burden of making the arrangements to find the mental strength for more than a couple of phone calls to her mother. Mária, on her part, appeared to have no desire to be involved with anything connected with her late son and no inkling about how her daughter felt about losing her brother.

When Rika went to see Mária the day after, she had been hoping for some opening up, some revelation of feelings by her mother. Especially, as Gyuri was at work. Over lunch, however, they spoke of inconsequential things and repeated variations of past conversations on uncontroversial topics, with no mention of anything personal. As they awkwardly skirted round the elephant-in-the-room subject of Gábor, suddenly Mária blurted out: 'You know, if Gyuri hadn't been around, I wouldn't be alive today.'

Rika felt shocked. 'What do you mean?'

'Gábor got into terrible rages and could be very rough ... thank God, Gyuri was there to protect me.'

'I know about your disagreements all those years ago, he mentioned it in his letters to me. But he wasn't violent ... it wasn't in his nature.'

'He was ... Gyuri is my witness ... I was covered in bruises, black and blue ...' Maria started crying.

Rika couldn't bear to see it and put her arms around her mother's shoulder. But she was angry at what her mother implied. She did not know how to defuse the situation without appearing to suggest that her mother was lying.

She tried to explain, 'My impression was that Gábor believed you didn't love him any more, he felt threatened by Gyuri and he didn't want to lose your love ... I think that may have been behind his behaviour ....'

It didn't work. 'It doesn't matter any more, there's no point in discussing it,' said Mária, drying her eyes, her habit of sweeping disturbing matters under the carpet unchanged.

On the plane returning to London the scene at her mother's kept replaying in Rika's mind. Her mother's insinuations were really insensitive, she thought, they were besmirching Gábor's memory and trying to score a point against somebody who could no longer answer back. Whatever happened to 'don't speak ill of the dead' and all that? Even if he'd been no angel, it would have been better to say nothing.

Her mother clearly regarded herself as a victim and was still fighting the battles of more than a decade and a half ago. Not speaking about the past did not mean that she had laid those conflicts to rest. She and Gyuri had a version of what happened, that was different from Gábor's. Who knows what was the truth?

Rika looked out of the plane's window at the crumpled brown-green mountains below, their boring shapes soothing her agitation. She was glad to be going back to the place she considered home and away once again from distressing emotions. She was toying with the idea that she didn't have to see her mother on future visits. What's the point if there's so much enmity between them? Her mother obviously saw her daughter as part of the hostile, opposite camp of her ex-husband and rebellious son, all the people who have deserted her.

21

Hope Over Experience

Straight after getting up, when the sun was already coming into his bedroom over the roof of the neighbour's house, Tamás went to make coffee. Not downstairs – he did not want to disturb Ildikó, who was sleeping late – but at the two-ring electric stove rigged up on top of a small fridge, next to the upstairs shower room. The walls around the stove were speckled with splashes of coffee, relics of previous explosions. Checking that he had the measures of ground coffee and water correct, and the top screwed on properly, he put the moka pot on the stove and went back to his room to collect his mug.

The mug lived on his bedside table, covered with a coaster, and it would go back there every morning, after he filled it with freshly-made coffee, added six teaspoons of sugar and drank it. No washing necessary, he insisted; the built-up sugary residue enhanced the taste of next day's coffee and it was protected from flies by the coaster. He would guard his mug against anybody who wanted to take it away to wash it.

Today promised to be another hot day. He padded through

the glazed corridor in his shorts and unbuttoned shirt, closed the panels that let in the cool air during the night and lowered the blinds. Already a bit late for this, he realised, it should have been done earlier. Before going to his computer room, he thought he'd better check on the cacti. He could not remember when he last watered them, so he went to collect some rainwater from the bucket on the terrace.

On his way back he noticed that the cat, Ildikó's latest rescue, had managed to sneak in, got trapped upstairs overnight and peed in a small crater of the uneven concrete floor. The little rascal! How come nobody noticed? The cat was hiding behind the cacti and when he opened the door to the stairs she darted off. He didn't want to wake his daughter, she had more than earned her lie-in. He dealt with the problem himself, quickly and decisively, by pouring bleach on top of the pungent liquid.

It was time he finally tackled the job he undertook two weeks ago for the local vet. Part of a year-long maintenance contract, one of his increasingly rare private works, to keep his hand in and supplement his pension. He had always thought he could repair anything, but this laptop defied him. He simply couldn't find the fault.

The small windowless room was getting hotter. He removed his black-framed spectacles and wiped his face with his shrugged-off shirt. He did not need the glasses, he could see better without them. His eyes, pale blue and watery, examined the adversary with renewed concentration. Turning the laptop over, he undid the four small screws he hadn't noticed before. The screwdriver was slippery in his hand, but soon the innards of the laptop were exposed and he was lost again in his world of idiosyncratic troubleshooting.

Ildikó appeared in the doorway an hour later asking what he wanted for lunch and reminding him of Rika's arrival. Her father's desk was covered by more dismantled parts than could possibly fit inside the laptop, but his face beamed with smug satisfaction.

Driving to Ferihegy to pick Rika up Tamás stayed on the old road. On the newly-finished, motorway-style access to the airport the police were always monitoring the traffic and his MOT was not up-to-date. He could not afford to renew it or to pay the fine if caught without having a valid one. An added bonus for taking the old road was that he could get away with *not* fastening his seatbelt, just draping it across his body. Making it look from a distance as if he'd complied with the regulations, while effectively rebelling against them. Like a lot of drivers did.

On the way back to his house Tamás talked to Rika about the end of his third marriage and the acrimonious divorce. He had no friends to confide in and didn't feel he could complain to his children about their mother, so the accumulated, pent-up bitterness poured out of him now.

'You know, I always said I didn't want to marry the Academy of Sciences, but her stupidity was sometimes staggering.'

Rika thought this evaluation of Éva was spot on and guessed that her father's choice of his third wife was not determined by his head but by another part of his anatomy. She said jokily, 'Maybe it would've been better if you *did* marry the Academy of Sciences.'

'And she so was malicious and manipulative! This woman totally ruined my relationship with my brother. She was the cause of our estrangement.'

'I didn't know about that,' said Rika, 'but I often wondered why Uncle Pál haven't been around since you and Éva got married.' When her father didn't explain, Rika realised this wasn't a conversation but an unburdening, and her assigned role was that of a silent confessor.

'She had affairs right from the beginning,' continued Tamás, tearing up. 'It was very humiliating. She'd put me through the wringer. You know, Marikám, I've been keeping a list of Éva's lovers over the years, all the people she cheated me with. You'd be surprised by the names on it.'

Did he know about the fling that Éva had with Gábor? wondered Rika. What Gábor confessed to her on her first visit back. Is that what her father was referring to? But she didn't ask. She'd rather not know.

'The only good thing that came out of this marriage are the children. They were the reason I put up with her behaviour for so long. And she was quite a good mother, while the kids were small.'

In the divorce settlement Éva demanded half of everything. Tamás argued that since the family home in Kőbánya had been originally bought by him, it shouldn't form part of the marital assets. 'I have only put her name onto the deeds later, when she nagged me, in order to avoid further arguments.' The family court, however, saw it differently. He got the house, where he lived with Ildikó and for a short while with Viki and her boyfriend. Éva walked away from the marriage with ownership of the weekend house in the Börzsöny hills.

After Éva had moved out and her salary had been taken out of the household income Tamás became increasingly hard up. Although he had a fairly good pension when he retired, over the years it was eroded by inflation. His private jobs also trickled to almost nothing the further he got into retirement.

He explained to Rika what'd been happening over the last few years. 'You know, after the regime change in 1990, there was this incredibly fast transformation to capitalism. Foreign enterprises moved in and bought up Hungarian ones. We all thought it was a good thing, to get rid of the command economy. And the people who got links to foreign or privatised businesses – like Andris – have been doing extremely well, earning western-level salaries. But everyone else, pensioners and people employed in factories or offices or shops, and even teachers and doctors, got poorer. Our incomes couldn't keep up with increasing prices. When I go shopping at PennyMarket I see grey-haired grannies begging at the door for the price of a couple of rolls and half-a-litre of milk.'

Ildiko still lived at home, studying at university and not only not able to pitch in with the household expenses, but having to be supported by Tamás. After Viki had got her first job as a doctor and rented a flat with her boyfriend, Balázs, she didn't have a lot to spare to help her father. Andris could've contributed regularly, but it didn't occur to him and Tamás's pride prevented asking his son. Rika gave her father money from time to time, but these were mere drops in the ocean, not making a substantial impact on the income versus outgoings imbalance.

The house was getting increasingly ramshackle, with one thing after another breaking down, and no money for proper repairs. It was all make-do and DIY mend. When the shower upstairs started to leak into one of the downstairs rooms, Tamás blamed it on the person who cleaned the gunge out from the shower-tray, and his 'repair' involved making the plughole almost clogged again with hair. Balázs jokily called Tamás's peculiar methods of dealing with problems 'human-scale solutions'.

After Tamás's old car had stopped running and he couldn't coax it back to life, he bought an even older, third-hand Škoda, because 'at least on this model I'm able to fix everything.' Even so, he only bothered to repair things that were absolutely essential. The front passenger door didn't open, so when he gave a lift to someone they had to sit at the back or had to bottom-shuffle into the front seat across from the driver's side. And trying to re-start the car on freezing winter days required cooperation from his passenger or whoever was around, to keep hitting a tube under the bonnet with a small hammer while Tamás repeatedly tried to turn on the ignition.

To reduce his bills Tamás resorted to another of his inventive problem-solving ways. The heating in the house being all electric and frighteningly expensive, he 'modified' the electricity supply coming into the property. After all he wasn't a qualified electric engineer for nothing. He re-wired the connection so that the incoming current usually by-passed the meter and only flowed through it a fraction of the time. He was careful to maintain a credible level of consumption in the winter months and undo his 'modification' in the summer.

Before going back to London Rika took her father and Ildikó out for a meal. Andris, away on a foreign trip, and Viki, working a long shift at the hospital, couldn't come. On the walk to a local restaurant they talked about their plans for the future.

'I would like to switch to vet school,' said Ildikó. Previously, after the *gimnázium*, she'd tried to get into the Veterinary College, but the requirements were high and the competition fierce. So she'd started a different university course, but her heart wasn't in it. 'I might take a year out and do the entry exam again. I want to work with animals.'

Ildikó's intentions were not really surprising, given the small menagerie she'd accumulated at home over the years, of which two dogs, several rescued stray cats, a rabbit and a tortoise still survived. But has she taken it into account that the financing of another course would prolong the burden on their father, wondered Rika silently.

'What about you, Apu? Any projects?'

'Well, now that I am a free man again, I may start dating to find a new partner,' said Tamás.

Rika was surprised. 'Considering your history of marriages, that would really be a triumph of hope over experience.'

Seeing the initial incomprehension on her father's face Rika realised that she spoke in English, which was how the thought came into her head. But with a little delay Tamás did work out the meaning of her words and buoyed up by this success he added, 'I would like to find somebody intelligent, attractive and certainly not older than forty.'

Has he lost touch with reality? thought Rika. He's over seventy, has he not learnt from past history? But to cheer her father up after the divorce and to give him a holiday, she invited him to London and bought him a plane ticket for the following spring.

*

I hope they're not going to postpone it again. I don't want to have starved myself once more for nothing. They call you at the last minute, early in the morning, just as you're about to leave for the hospital, and tell you it's off, they haven't got a bed for you that day. Then they ring you a couple of days later, and you cannot eat again for a day. And all the water you have to drink. I haven't had to pee so much in my whole life!

They tell me it may not be too late. Though our GP missed it in the manual examination, but then he was looking for signs of something else. Which wasn't there. And what *was* there was just beyond his reach, as it turned out.

After the GP gave me the all clear I still told Rika I couldn't go to London. I told her my prostrate trouble – as I thought of it at that time – might flare up while I visited her and I didn't want her having to fork out for emergency treatment for me. Which would've been very costly for a foreign national.

By that time I'd already cashed in the plane ticket she bought for me. I didn't tell her that. Nor that I spent the money to pay overdue bills.

It was good to have a doctor in the family when the more worrying symptoms came along. Viki is such a fighter! How she

273

accused the GP of professional negligence and then got me an appointment with the leading colorectal surgeon. All the tests organised in a week. And the diagnosis which explained all the previous signs and symptoms.

They think it may have been caught in time. But the operation will be a major one, they say, and quite risky. Viki said she would give up smoking if I came through it all right.

But I'm not too worried. They'll cut you open, unpack everything inside and remove the things that shouldn't be there. And there will be a long recovery. Probably radiotherapy as well. But I will beat it. I'm determined to live till a hundred.

*

Tamás came through the operation successfully. The surgeon was able to cut out the malignant growth without removing too much of the colon. Viki stopped smoking, Andris organised things in the background and Ildikó looked after her father day after day, her gentle nagging boosting his spirit.

Rika visited her father during his convalescence. Tamás lay propped up in bed, pyjama top unbuttoned, one hand protecting the huge bandage on his stomach, the other clutching the TV remote. He was still weak but from his semi-horizontal position he commanded all around him and enjoyed being the centre of attention. To enquiries about his health he replied, 'You know, I've had an encounter with Jack the Ripper.'

There followed a short radiation therapy, which Tamás treated as a subsidiary battle to get over and he was still resolved to come out of it all victorious. The next CT scan, however, showed that the cancer had metastasised. The surgeon was brutally frank with him, and declared another operation and chemotherapy his only possible hope.

A week later at Christmas with his children around him, Tamás looked shocked and was uncharacteristically silent. He couldn't believe that his determination alone had not been enough to defeat the illness. It started to dawn on him that he may not survive.

The new year brought another operation, more drastic than the first, resulting in Tamás having to wear a colostomy bag. This meant further psychological devastation for him, signalling, as he saw it, the end of his sex life. Who would want to date a man carrying his shit around with him? That in his seventies his chances of romance were already fairly low, didn't occur to him.

After the recovery from the second operation, several cycles of chemotherapy were scheduled. As the first few sessions were not as bad as he had feared, Tamás's determination to overcome the cancer returned. And since the date in May for Viki's long planned wedding was falling into a break between cycles, they did not cancel it. It represented a hope for the future, a wish that the illness could be kept at bay and a dream for a grandchild.

Viki was a radiant bride and Balázs a handsome, slimmed-down-for-the-occasion groom. The wedding ceremonies – civil and religious – went off well, despite the mother of the bride, estranged from her daughter, not being invited and the father of the bride trying to hide his despair at the prognosis of his illness.

At the wedding party in the evening Andris's date was a vivacious redhead, Zsuzsa, whom he had recently met in an on-line chat room. Tamás, after some champagne and a couple of dances with his son's beautiful date, seemed much cheered up and his gloomy expression disappeared.

In December Andris was promoted by his company and sent to Johannesburg to be the Business Development Manager for the whole Southern African region. Although this posting was considered a dangerous one and not to everyone's taste, it was a sign of his rapid rise in the organisation, and he was nothing if not ambitious. But he didn't want to put an end to his relationship with Zsuzsa, so he proposed marriage to allow them to go together as a couple.

Under the pressure of time the wedding was organised quickly, attended by just a couple of their friends as witnesses, and he only told his parents about it after the event. Éva's self-importance was greatly offended by this and she blamed Zsuzsa for coming between her son and herself. She also insinuated, to all who couldn't avoid listening, that Zsuzsa only married Andris for his money, and had also thrown this accusation repeatedly into her daughter-in-law's face.

In the following spring Rika visited her father in time for his birthday. Tamás had a chemo session scheduled that day, so she made her way to her father's house by taking the airport bus, the metro and another bus. As she was approaching the gate she saw Tamás getting out of a car and with the help of his son-in-law making his way into the yard. At the foot of the stairs, however, his legs gave way and Balázs had to carry him upstairs to his bedroom.

The invasion of Iraq by western coalition forces had started earlier that month. As Tamás's life became dominated by his illness and his personal realm had shrunk drastically, he got hooked on the news broadcasts from around the world. He couldn't get enough of these programs, switching compulsively from CNN to Deutsche Welle, from the BBC World Service to Austrian news. Rika watched the reports with her father in his bedroom in between accompanying him for medical appointments.

The treatment he was getting now was based on an Israeli drug, which was in the process of being evaluated and not yet fully licensed in Hungary. Viki pulled some strings to get her father into the trial as a participant and Andris sourced the drug from abroad to speed things up.

Tamás was getting increasingly reluctant to submit to a cure he felt was worse than the problem. It wasn't only the vomiting, his remaining hair falling out, his rapid weight loss and general weakness. 'I can feel the poison eating me from inside, corroding my veins, burning my flesh,' he said. Before each dreaded session he had to psych himself up, telling himself he had to persevere, he had nothing to lose, and that there was still a tiny flicker of hope that he might come through.

When next July Rika went to Budapest, Viki and Balázs picked her up at the airport. They told her that Tamás's condition had deteriorated to the point that he was hardly getting out of bed, not eating much and constantly having to take pain killers. Although earlier Viki had managed to get her father into yet another experimental treatment programme, Tamás stopped going after the first session.

Viki had a little bit of good news in the general gloom. She was pregnant, about a month-and-a-half gone, she said. 'I have a friend at the hospital who is a radiographer and she confirmed it early with an ultrasound.' But after a number of miscarriages in the previous two years, Viki was very cautious. Arriving at their father's house she would not come in with Rika, and explained that she was afraid of catching toxoplasmosis. 'You know, Ildikó is not very scrupulous about cleaning out the cats' litter tray. I don't want to risk infection in the first trimester and losing this baby too.'

The burden of constant care for Tamás had fallen fully on the shoulders of his youngest child, still living at home. Ildikó had dropped out of her university course and was now working in a bookshop. All her free time was consumed by looking after her invalid father. She may not have been too keen on cleaning and tidying generally, but now she had to deal with much more unpleasant things: emptying of her father's 'bags' or cleaning up vomit. Rika thought Viki should appreciate what Ildikó's doing and not be so judgemental.

Rika was shocked to see how thin her always plump father had become. She remembered the CT scan taken after his first chemotherapy cycle. Then her father's silhouette on the image was a barrel pulled in at the middle into an hourglass shape by his belt. Now the same belt would fall off him even on the smallest setting.

One day to tempt her father's appetite she suggested making a lunch of scrambled eggs with spicy sausages. She asked her father how many eggs he wanted in his portion, and he said six. This is wishful thinking, thought Rika, not realistic; he remembers his healthy appetite of many years ago. But she cooked it to his requirements. Sitting up in bed he ate less than a quarter of the food on his plate before he said he couldn't eat any more.

Mid-morning on the day of her scheduled return to London Rika went into his father's room and found him asleep with the television on. As she took the remote from his hand to switch the TV off he woke up and asked her to sit down on the edge his bed.

He started talking about his last wishes. 'You'll all inherit this house together, but it shouldn't be sold after my death, otherwise Ildikó will have nowhere to live.'

'We don't have to discuss that now, you'll get better', said Rika, thinking, if we acknowledge that his death is near, does it mean we've given up hope he may recover?

'But if the house has to be sold,' continued Tamás, not hearing his daughter, 'if there's no other way out, it shouldn't be sold cheap. I know some developers are interested in the plot and will pay a good price.'

Focusing on practicalities, Rika asked, 'Do you want to put it down in writing, like in a will, exactly what you want, after ... after ... when you're not around? So that everybody knows.'

'No, no, that's not necessary. I'm telling you now. ... I'm very worried about Ildikó. Andris and Viki are both set up for life, but Ildi, how will she manage after I'm gone? I don't just mean financially. ... She hasn't had much luck with boys, but she will make someone a nice little wife, she's such a good cook. And you saw how well she's been looking after me.

You should all help her, and help each other. You children were the most important thing in my life, what I wanted most of all. ... I hope you know that I love you, ... all of you ... even if I didn't show it, couldn't show it.'

This was most uncharacteristic of her father. He had never been demonstrative, he had never done emotions, he had never ever told her that he loved her. This frightened Rika. She realised that the conversation they were having was her father's final goodbye to her. Does he sense the end approaching?

The phone rang. The taxi was waiting at the gate to take her to the airport.

What was she to do? She had to leave now and didn't know if she would see him again alive. Her heart felt as if it was squeezed, wrung out by an invisible hand. Was this what people referred to when they said their heart was breaking?

They hugged each other for a long time and Rika felt her father's fragile shoulders under her hands. She promised she would come back as soon as she could. As she was leaving the room, turning away to hide her tears, Tamás addressed his last words to her back: 'Look after the six-week-old'.

Rika didn't understand what he meant. But later, in the taxi, she figured out that what her father hinted at was Viki's pregnancy, that six-week-old embryo of hope. The grandchild that he would probably not know.

22

Arriving and Leaving

After the death of her father Rika's trips to Budapest became less frequent. She still went back to see her mother, because she felt guilty if she didn't, but couldn't face it too often, certainly not every year. The prospect of having almost identical, pointless conversations every single time, of feeling her mother's silent disapproval and Gyuri's barely concealed distrust of her and their lack of interest whenever she talked about her own life, made her want to repeat the experience as seldom as possible.

She was grateful that her mother's marriage to Gyuri had effectively relieved her of the burden of caring for an elderly parent that she, as her mother's only surviving child, could have expected to fall on her sooner or later. Isn't it lucky for me, she thought, that Gyuri is younger than my mother and will look after her till the end?

But each time she did go to Budapest she had to lighten these duty visits, making them bearable by adding other purposes to her journeys, such as seeing her sisters or making it a short holiday.

Viki happily managed to carry to term the baby she had been expecting when their father died, and gave birth to a boy. Two years later she and Balázs had a little girl. Then six months after that, not seeing much professional future in Hungary, Viki left with her family to take up a post in a French hospital.

Ildikó had stayed on in the family house for a while and was finding it hard to re-boot her life after the illness and death of her beloved father. Having drifted for a long time between dead-end jobs she'd eventually got a good position in a bank, monitoring credit-card fraud, which made use of her excellent English. She had also started a part-time university course in animal breeding. After several unsuccessful attempts to get into vet school, this was the route taking her closest to her passion of working with animals.

Meanwhile in London Rika had found full-time and permanent work as an administrator in local government. It wasn't her dream job to be an office-cog, what was required of her was far below what she was capable of, but after many years of part-time and temporary employment, she could finally escape from a frugal, precarious way of living and even have proper holidays.

With this measure of stability in her life she started on-line dating to find a life partner, following many years of chance failures. On various dating sites she came across a lot of unsuitable candidates. Some just wanted casual sex. Several were strangers to the truth, like the guy who on face-to-face meeting proved to be the father of the one portrayed on the website or the man who boasted about his athletic figure and turned out to be grossly obese. Many of them had ingrained commitment issues. Luckily none tried to swindle her out of her money, but that may have been because they realised early on she didn't have much.

After having to kiss a lot of frogs that failed to turn into princes, she changed the strap-line on her Guardian Soulmates profile page. This called forth a reply from a guy who hadn't previously been identified by the algorithm as a possible match. From his reactions and messages Rika instantly felt they were on the same wavelength, they had a rapport. When after a couple of weeks of promising email exchanges they met in real life, Martin turned out to be exactly like the persona he presented on-line and they started seeing each other.

From the next summer onwards many of her annual holidays became a combination of visiting her mother with Martin – his presence served as Rika's excuse for limiting the frequency and duration of these occasions – and of showing him a little of her native country and the places where she grew up.

The underpass in front of the Eastern Railway Station was unexpectedly crowded and coming out of the metro station Rika and Martin had to meander on their way to the upstairs ticket office. Their feet had to find the empty spaces on the floor, stepping left and right, weaving in and out between people sleeping on the bare pavement, among families huddled together on toy-strewn blankets or in front of camping tents. Towels, T-shirts and baby grows were drying in the sun on the railings framing the wide stairs to the main entrance of the station.

They had to come to the railway station. For this summer of 2015 they'd planned and organised a three-centre holiday in central Europe. They had flown to Budapest the day before, then in a few days they would take the train to Vienna, followed by another to Prague, from where they would fly back to London. Rika had managed to book everything on-line in the UK, but their seat reservation for the Budapest-Vienna express had to be done in person.

Before arriving in Budapest Rika had no idea that Hungary was this much in the frontline of the European migrant crisis. The media in the UK overwhelmingly focused on refugees arriving in the countries of the Mediterranean. But Hungary was now a member of the EU, Rika realised, and people coming from the Middle East by the relatively safe land-route could travel onward without further checks within the Schengen Area. These refugees all wanted to go to western Europe and Hungary was only a staging post on their journey.

In the full to overflowing booking office, where the sticky, thirty-degrees August heat was not eased by ventilation let alone air conditioning, Rika tore off a numbered ticket from a machine and saw that twenty-six people were ahead of them in the queue. There were only four booking windows open and when somebody finally reached them, it took them ages to complete their business. All the seats in the room were taken and people were sitting on the floor or leaning against the walls. To avoid the stale, sweaty air Rika and Martin stayed near the door, waiting for their turn.

'Want to buy tickets to Germany,' said a voice in broken English behind their back. Turning around and stepping out of the way they saw a dark skinned, dark haired man in a sweatshirt coming into the booking office. Martin, always ready to get into friendly conversations with strangers, explained to the man how he needed to queue before he could buy the train ticket.

The man told them that he'd came from Aleppo with his wife and two young children. Their house was reduced to rubble after an air raid. 'Mother killed, father killed,' he said, wiping his eyes with the back of his hand. They had been travelling for weeks, he'd lost count for how long, by bus, on foot, by boat and train, and just wanted to get to Germany. 'Mrs Merkel welcome us. Mrs Merkel want us come'.

More than an hour later having got their seat reservation Rika and Martin emerged from the railway station through the now much busier underpass. Volunteers wearing Migrant Aid t-shirts were handing out bottles of water, apples, boxes of pizza and small bags of toiletries to the refugees, who waited patiently in a queue, while children played hide and seek, snaking through the long line of adult legs. In the middle of a circle of onlookers a doctor was bandaging up the leg of a middle aged woman lying on a bloody towel on the pavement. Behind them men were rummaging through of heaps of donated clothing, exclaiming triumphantly when they found trousers or shoes in the right size to replace their journey-tattered ones.

Lines of police watched from a distance. Local people hurrying about their daily business, dragged staring youngsters behind them and gave the foreigners a wide berth. On the street level, at the side of the square Rika spotted a large poster, apparently left behind after a recent anti-migrant demonstration. It said, 'Hungary is not a refugee camp, there is no room here for raging hoards of migrants.' She translated the words for Martin, and was ashamed that people in the country she grew up in held such views.

After booking their seats on the express they went to see Rika's mother. As usual they were welcomed by lunch, but unusually it was Gyuri who was busy in the kitchen.

'I can't do much any more,' explained Mária, 'no matter how I try. I just can't. It's lucky that Gyuri is handy in the kitchen. He can cook, if I show him how to.'

In the previous years Mária had a litany of health problems: a heart attack, followed by stent insertion, a stroke and carotid artery surgery, chronic lung disease and several slow-healing fractures. Despite all these, frail now in her eighty-fifth year and rattling with essential medication, she still had a fifteen-a-day habit. And when Rika chided her mother for smoking, she quipped 'You have to die of *something*.'

Gyuri came into the living room with a bottle of *pálinka* and four shot glasses.

'I don't want any, Gyurikám,' said Mária, 'you know how it upsets my stomach.'

'Nonsense. It'll give you an appetite.' insisted Gyuri, filling the glasses to the brim.

'This is the Hungarian tradition,' he explained to Martin. '*Egészségedre!*'

'Eges-sheged-re.' Martin tried to wrap his tongue around the Hungarian vowels.

After they clinked their glasses, Gyuri poured his drink down his throat in one swift movement and went back to the kitchen, taking the bottle with him.

The strong home-distilled liquor burnt Rika's mouth and

she saw that Martin was also struggling with the *pálinka*. Mária took a sip, which almost immediately made her gag. Covering her mouth with one hand she struggled to get up from the sofa and, waving away Rika's help, she made her way to the bathroom, with small steps, supporting herself on door jambs and walls with her other hand. Through the closed door they heard retching noises, but no reply when Rika asked her mother if she was all right.

Mária was still out of the room when Gyuri came in carrying the soup tureen to the table. 'Don't worry about your mother,' he said to Rika, 'she often has this problem. And the doctors don't know what causes it, they just say it's age related. We should start without her.'

When Mária returned to the table she looked subdued and exhausted. She ate her clear soup greedily, spooning it down at great speed, as if she had been starving for days. After the soup though she didn't wanted to eat much else. 'Gyurikám, you've given me such an enormous portion, I can't manage that,' she protested when Gyuri'd served her a spoonful of mashed potatoes and a chicken drumstick. She left half of it behind, uneaten on her plate.

No wonder she's so thin, if she doesn't eat, thought Rika. Seeing her mother's skeletal figure, revealed as nothing but skin and bones in the sleeveless vest and shorts she wore in the hot weather, was very upsetting.

Rika and Martin mentioned what they have seen at the Eastern Railway Station.

'Oh, this has been going on for weeks now,' said Gyuri. 'At first there was sympathy with the migrants, because the general public understood that they don't want to stay, they want to travel on to Western Europe. But as the numbers camping out around railway stations grew, the police became increasingly unable to control the situation.'

'The people who live nearby are frightened of these strangers and had enough of this unhappy situation,' cut in Mária.

'Then the government, our *King Viktor*' – Gyuri pronounced the name with contemptuous emphasis – 'said that these are not really refugees, they are economic migrants and terrorists, and we should get rid of them before they can destroy us and our culture.'

'I don't understand, anyway, what makes people leave their own country, why they want to go to a place where they are not welcome,' said Mária.

Rika couldn't leave her mother's words without comment. 'These people are escaping from a war, Anyukám, their homes were destroyed and many of their relatives were killed. Do you think they would undertake such dangerous journeys if their lives were not threatened, if they could see a future in their homeland?'

But there was no reaction from her mother or Gyuri, and with this rhetorical question hanging in the air, the subject was abandoned.

Gyuri wasn't really interested in the fate of the migrants because he had his own important news to tell, and after lunch, savouring his guests' present of a honeyed apricot liqueur, he embarked on his account.

'You may wander why in the middle of the week I'm not at work. Well, I'm unemployed. I was made redundant in May, because Michelin has closed down its factory in Budapest.'

'Oh, my god!' exclaimed Rika. 'How? I mean, why?'

'The factory is in a fairly central area, surrounded by buildings on all sides, with no room for expansion or development. It's also a prime site, next to the Aréna Plaza and opposite the Puskás Stadium. Rumour has it that our football-mad *King* has his eyes on the plot and wants to build sport facilities there, that's why he agreed to Michelin moving their production somewhere else.'

'Where are they moving production? Abroad?' asked Rika.

'No, to another of their factories, that's been making different types of tyres, near Debrecen,' said Gyuri. 'At first I thought it could all work out well for me. We could move back to my village – my mother would love that – and I could commute to work from there, it's not so far. But your mother wouldn't hear about it, so that was the end of that.'

'I told Gyuri categorically, you move back if you want to, I'm not standing in your way, but I'm staying put, I'm not going anywhere!' Mária added with feeling.

'So are you getting unemployment benefit now?' asked Martin, after Rika's back-and-forth translations.

'Nah, I won't bother with that, you can't live on that pittance and it's very humiliating. They gave us redundancy packages, almost worth two years of average salary. Mind you, they had to, kicking more than five hundred of us workers onto the street.'

'And they'll provide courses to re-train and help you find a new job,' chipped in Mária.

'Well, I don't know if I can still learn new things at fifty-six. I wasn't a very good student at school. Besides, when jobs are advertised, they don't want applicants over fifty, so it's basically hopeless,' said Gyuri.

'But you have to try, don't you? Don't be a defeatist.' Rika was worried. How would her mother and Gyuri manage to live solely on her mother's pension, if he couldn't or wouldn't get a new job?

'I will. But first I'm going to have a long rest and a few holidays. I've earned it, I've been working without substantial breaks, on rotating shifts, since I was eighteen. And the redundancy money will last for a while.'

While in Budapest Rika and Martin also went to see Ildikó. She was the only one of Rika's siblings still based in Hungary, as Andris and Viki had been working abroad for several years.

Ildikó was living with her partner, Bence, and their three-year-old son Ádám in a privately rented flat near a railway line. Although Rika had visited them the year before, to her nephew she was no less unfamiliar than the strange man now accompanying her. Ádám shyly hid behind his father's legs when the visitors came in. Martin crouched down to toddler level and greeted him in his best Hungarian, 'Szia Ádám.' The little boy burst into tears.

'I think he's frightened by Martin's moustache,' said Ildikó. 'In the kindergarten he's surrounded by women and he doesn't meet a lot of people outside the family.'

They all settled down on the long battered sofa in the main

room. Protectively flanked by his parents and having been assured by them that Martin was not a monster, Ádám stopped crying, but continued to look warily at the guests. He only left the safety of his father's side when his Aunt Rika produced from her rucksack his birthday present, the long hankered after Dino Rescue Patroller. He'd been pestering his parents for it for weeks.

The little boy's eyes lit up and he darted over where his aunt and the man with the moustache were sitting at the sofa's other end. Forgetting his fear of Martin, he sank down in front of him on the carpet, trying to tear the package apart. When he couldn't open his present fast enough, he lifted the box towards Martin with both hands, asking for help, 'Dino, Dino!'

The ice was broken. Bence joined his son and soon all three males – from three different generations –were sitting on the floor engaged in the unboxing, assembling and operating the Dino Rescue Patroller. Martin tried to show Ádám what needed to be done and, when his gestures weren't enough, Bence came to the rescue, translating Martin's words for his son.

Leaving the boys to their toys Rika followed her sister to the kitchen where Ildikó was starting to prepare lunch.

'Can I do something to help?' asked Rika.

'No, thanks, it's all under control. I've already made a potato salad and just need to fry the chicken. *Rántott csirke* is Bence's favourite, it's our regular weekend treat. But you can make some coffee. Ádám woke us up at dawn and I really need a pick-me-up.'

While Rika prepared coffee in the stove-top moka pot, Ildikó flattened a couple of chicken breasts with the metal-spiked meat hammer until they were twice their original size. She then filled three soup-plates with flour, beaten eggs and breadcrumbs, and with quick, practised movements dipped the chicken breasts and a few thighs and drumsticks into them, one by one. After all the pieces have been coated and lined up on a tray, she fried them in oil, two or three at a time, as she talked to Rika about the current trouble with their landlord.

'From October he wants to double the rent we're paying now, because he says there was no rise in the past three years. But our salaries haven't increased during this time, and we won't be able to afford it, it's just too much.'

'So what are you going to do? Can you look for somewhere else to rent?'

'We *have* been looking, but no luck. The problem is people don't want a couple with a young child. God knows what they're worried about, afraid that the child will eat the wallpaper?'

At lunch Ádám was sitting in his booster seat at the head of the table, his whims attended to by his doting parents on either side. Cutting up his food exactly the way he liked, changing his drinking cup to his favourite-of-the-moment, coaxing him to drink his juice, and dangling the promise of ice cream to get him eat up his food. Over the meal any talk not relating to him was prone to interruptions and soon abandoned.

It wasn't until Ádám was having his afternoon nap, that the adults finally had a chance for a grown up conversation. They also had to close the windows, despite the heat, because the trains rattling past every twenty minutes, even on a Saturday, drowned out their words and they were afraid that raising their voices would wake the child sleeping in the same room.

It struck Rika that Ildikó and Bence's life was entirely dominated by their little boy, with not much time and energy left for an adult life, for their own interests and pursuits. But maybe that's how it always is for parents, she thought, and someone childless like me simply can't understand it.

'I am very grateful to you, Martin and Rika, for this opportunity to speak English,' started Bence, a little formally, as they were settling down on the sofa after lunch. 'I've been doing online courses for a while to refresh my pitiful schoolboy knowledge, but until today I haven't realised how much I *do* understand or how much I'm *actually* able to say.'

Ildikó came in with the coffee. 'I've been telling Bence that he has nothing to worry about, he just needs confidence and more practice.'

'Bence, I can tell you that your English is much better than some people's who speak it as their first language,' said Martin.

'Thank you for saying that. I wanted to improve because I want to work in England. I applied through EUWork and they got me a job in a Distribution Centre. I will start in October.'

'Wow, that's great news, what a surprise!' exclaimed Rika. 'But what about Ildi and Ádám? Are you all going together?'

'No, I will go first and if things work out, they will join me in a few months. Until then they will stay with Ildi's mother. You know, I suppose, that we have to move out of this flat.'

'Beyond our difficulties with finding somewhere to live, we don't see much point in staying in this country,' explained Ildikó. 'This rotten, corrupt government has stolen our future, cosied up to the Russians again and the system is so manipulated that there's no hope for change.'

'I know it is going to be very hard at the beginning,' added Bence. 'I will be an unskilled warehouse worker, on the minimum wage, but I reckon we will still be better off in the long run than we are now. So much of what you earn here is taken away from you. And one is able to withstand a lot of hardship if the prospects at the end are good.'

'And ultimately,' said Ildikó, 'we do it to give Ádám a better future, better than what we could have here.'

On the day of their departure for Vienna Rika and Martin could hardly get to their platform for the sea of people that had flooded the railway station. It looked like all the refugees that were camped out in front of the building a few days ago were now wanting to get away by train. Above the the heads of the crowd here and there an up-stretched arm could be seen clutching a bundle of documents, the owner of the arm clearing the way for a closely following group of people. There were also rows of armed policemen, keeping an eye on the melee in the background, by both sides of the great vaulted hall.

Rika and Martin fought their way to the carriage in which they reserved seats. The door was guarded by a railway official, who inspected their tickets minutely before allowing them onboard. Moving through the train to find their seats they were coming face to face with a contraflow of people, a group of women and children clustering around a male figure, who evidently stole through the not-so-efficiently-checked other entry to the carriage. They were followed in hot pursuit by another conductor, shouting behind their backs in Hungarian, 'Syrian people, Syrian people, get off the train!'

If she knows these people are Syrian how does she expect them to understand her, thought Rika, and was about to step forward and offer herself as an interpreter, when she noticed several armed policeman behind the conductor. They demanded to see the identity papers and the train tickets of the people who slipped aboard unchecked. After a great deal of cacophony, cries and tears, with a lot of pushing and showing, the interlopers were taken off the train. As she was putting her suitcase onto the rack Rika looked out of the window and saw that the group were led away from the platforms and escorted out of the station.

A few minutes later the Vienna Express pulled out of the Eastern Railway Station. All the seats in the carriage were occupied and none of the passengers appeared to be Syrian or refugees.

As the express was approaching the Austrian border Rika had a strong sense of déjà vu and waves of nervousness rose from her stomach. Although the train they were travelling on today was far less rickety than the one she defected on almost forty years ago, although at this time she was not trying to escape illegally, terrified of discovery and punishment, the superficial resemblance of the situations, then and now, filled her with hard-to-explain apprehension. Taking deep breaths she reminded herself that these days the trains don't even stop on the border for passport checks.

'Look, Rika! Over there, under the trees. Look at those people!' Martin's exclamation nudged Rika out of her silent anxiety. Glimpsed through the sparse woods in the near distance they saw scattered groups of men, women, children and even what looked like somebody in a wheelchair, moving parallel with the train in a westerly direction.

'It must be those refugees we saw in front of the railway station,' speculated Martin.

'Yes, or others just like them. The lucky ones must've been allowed to get onto trains after hanging around for days,' said Rika. 'But I've read that a lot of them became impatient with waiting and started to walk from Budapest towards the western border. That's 170 kilometres away! And now buses specially chartered by civil organisations are picking them up along the journey and bring them here close to the border.'

The scene fleetingly witnessed from the speeding train suddenly conjured up in her mind others that played out over the very same border. Surrogate memories made up of family stories, archive films and survivors' reminiscences were now superimposed on each other, like double exposures on an old-fashioned film camera. Ghost visions of her mother, aunt and grandparents fleeing the Russian advance at the end of the Second World War. Black and white mental footage of dissidents escaping after the crushed 1956 revolution. Different ages and seasons, but the lot of defectors, refugees or migrants – however they may be defined and labelled – essentially hadn't changed much, it seemed to her.

The train was soon racing through Austrian territory, trying to outrun the dark clouds chasing them. Before they had reached Vienna the storm broke, washing away the oppressive summer heatwave. By the time they arrived the rain had stopped, the pavement in front of the station glistened and steam rose hazily from the heat-saturated surfaces. Outside, sheltering under the projecting canopy, groups of people were queuing up at food-laden tables, under banners of FLÜCHTLINGE WILLKOMMEN.

Acknowledgements

This book would not have come into being without The Novel Studio course at City, University of London. I would like to thank the Course Director, Emily Pedder, and tutors Emma Sweeney, Rebekah Lattin-Rawstone and Kiare Ladner for helping us fledgeling novelists to develop our skills. Getting feedback from my peers on the course was also invaluable – especial thanks due to Lucy Blincoe, Nola d'Enis, Seema Clear, Michael Lawson and Rhidian Wynn Davies.

For his unfailing support throughout the book's long gestation – lending a sympathetic yet critical ear, patiently answering my weird grammar queries and helping with formatting and graphic design – my heartfelt thanks go to Marshall Colman.